RED READER™

POE
A COLLECTION

Introductions and Annotations by Richard Marcus
Edited by Kara L. Quinn

TEACHER'S
Discovery™
©2003 American Eagle Co.

ISBN: 0-7560-0201-X

INTRODUCTION

QUESTION: How many writers have their face on the cover of The Beatles' *Sgt. Pepper* Album; are in *Looney Tunes* cartoons; are featured on *The Simpson's*; have had dozens of modern singers, including a heavy metal band, put their words to music; and have an NFL team, The Baltimore Ravens, named after one of their poems?

ANSWER: Nobody but Edgar Allan Poe. Oh, and add to the above that every year there are dozens of books and articles written about him; he's had his short stories turned into hundreds of TV shows, movies, and plays; and his books have never been out of print (Whew!).

If you also take into account that his entire writing career was only 15 years in length and that he lived over 150 years ago, it's even more amazing.

Now, just about everybody's heard of Edgar Allan Poe. Usually it's because of one of three things:

1. His classic horror stories. He liked to call his supernatural stories "grotesques" and his totally gross horror stories "arabesques."
2. His poem "The Raven," one of the best known in the English language, has been interpreted to mean many things. Some critics believe that at its core it is the expression of a deep love, lost forever. Others feel that it is more Poe exposing his own crippling, life-long depression. It's also, arguably, one of the most parodied poems in American literature.
3. His detective mysteries. With "The Murders in the Rue Morgue," he literally invented both the detective genre and the eccentric detective character, which countless other writers have copied, including the author of Sherlock Holmes.

THE CRITICS

The first thing I'm going to do below is to quote some of the many critics who have spent years studying Poe. A lot of them disagree about just what Edgar was up to. Now, trust me on this; it's going to help you later.

Harold Bloom, probably one of the foremost literary analysts in America, wrote that "Critics, even good ones, admire Poe's stories for some of the oddest reasons" and that "Poe authentically frightens children" (Let me add "adults" to that). He also writes that "Ralph Waldo Emerson, for better or worse, was and is the mind of America. But Poe was and is our hysteria. Our uncanny unanimity (unity) in our repressions" (those secret thoughts that we hide). In other words, Poe is the guy who wrote about some of our deepest and most terrifying thoughts. Things we don't want to admit. However, why he did this, his own motivation, is still up for grabs.

The very talented writer Richard Wilbur cites some critics who think Poe's work (I love this, even though I don't agree) was "Nothing more than complicated machines for saying 'Boo!'" One critic, Marie Bonaparte, who explored Poe's work using a psychoanalytical approach, wrote that "If we find Poe unintelligible (unknowable) we should congratulate ourselves, since if we could understand him it would be proof of our abnormality."

Other experts call his characters (and him) "vampires" and "conscious and brilliant psychological symbols of human depravity," an "utterly self-obsessed wanderer through the dark side of human nature." And other critics believe just the opposite: "A believer in a peculiar kind of transcendental human salvation."

Elizabeth Browning, the famous poet, noted that Poe's review of a book she wrote read almost like there were two completely different people writing alternate paragraphs of the criticism. That's probably the closest to what many feel is the truth.

Poe was first truly appreciated by the Romantic French writers such as Verlaine and Rimbaud, having been discovered by the French poet Charles Baudelaire. These dynamic young European writers saw that Poe was fearlessly gazing at the human mind in a way no one had ever before dared. They saw his writing, his understanding of the human psyche, as "perfect." Baudelaire's translation and publication of Poe in the 1850s made him the first American author to be widely read outside the United States.

What I hope has come across here is that there are as many interpretations of what he was saying as there are critics. Some think he was totally in control of everything he wrote, that he was objective and calculating. Others believe that every character he wrote about was himself, that every fear, every anguish, and every murder committed on the page was literary revenge for all the injustices, real and imagined, against him. They're probably all a bit correct.

The good thing about all these professionals and experts disagreeing is that it gives you the freedom to draw your own conclusions about him (Hey, even if everybody agreed, you can still have your own opinion). In other words, any way you "get" Poe, feel his stories, and more importantly, any place his stories take you inside your own mind, is valid. That seems to be one of the major (but not the only) thrusts of his work: to take people on an emotional trip inside their own heads. To Poe, attempting to find the charged emotion was the ultimate purpose and truth of art, as was trying to relieve his own very tortured mind of his pain and anger. You might even add that he also had a really weird sense of humor. But then again, that's just my opinion.

POE'S LIFE

One other thing about Poe which seems tragically modern was the catastrophic misfortunes, addictions, self-destruction, and pain that haunted his own life. It equals the kind of accounts of the most brokenhearted, drug-dependent rock stars portrayed on E Channel's *True Hollywood Stories*. Most critics do agree that it was from this unlucky life that he got the material for his darkest works.

Poe was born in Boston, Massachusetts, on January 19, 1809. His parents were very young actors at a time when the profession was despised and paid very poorly. His dad, an alcoholic, abandoned the family soon after Edgar's birth and was never heard from again. His mother died soon after of tuberculosis. One account has it that when she died, Poe was left alone, overnight, in the room with his mother's body. He was three, and psychologists would now agree that he was old enough to be affected for the rest of his life.

He was taken into the home of John and Frances Allan. John was a wealthy merchant in Richmond, Virginia. They were childless. John was by all accounts a very cold and self-righteous individual. Poe did get along with Frances. She was gentle and much more affectionate than her husband. She was also supposedly accident prone and ill for many months at a time.

Although John Allan and Edgar did not get along, Poe took "Allan" as his middle name. Between 1815 and 1820, he was raised in England. The crash of the tobacco market forced the family to return to America.

When Poe entered the University of Virginia in 1826 at the age of seventeen, Allan gave him only a small allowance. He was well liked but gambled and ran his debts over $2,000, a fortune in 1826, which John Allan refused to pay. One other aspect of this time was his affection for his friend Rob Stanard and Rob's mother Jane Stanard who, it is said, bore a striking resemblance to Poe's own mother and to Frances Allan. Stanard died, insane, from a variety of mental and physical problems about a year after they met. This was the second loss of a mother figure for Poe.

At this time, Poe's drinking became a serious problem. Allan withdrew Poe from school, and Poe came home disgraced. He soon left and went to Boston in 1827, where he persuaded a printer to issue a pamphlet of his poems called *Tamerlane and Other Poems*. Credit was given simply to "A Bostonian." The subject was of "an orphanlike figure of uncertain parentage." In 1829, Frances Allan, his beloved stepmother, died of tuberculosis. It was another crushing blow.

Poe spent a short time at the United States Military Academy at West Point. He did well in some of his studies but couldn't take the discipline and purposely got himself court-marshalled. At the same time, John Allan re-married and his new wife gave birth to a boy. John Allan then disowned Edgar (Note: You might want to keep this in mind when reading Poe's stories of revenge).

His first success as a writer came in 1833, when he entered a short-story contest and won a prize of 50 dollars for the story "MS. Found in a Bottle."

In 1835, he became the editor of the *Southern Literary Messenger*. At that time, he also married his cousin Virginia Clemm, who was only a few days short of her 14th birthday. From what he and others have written about their relationship, it seems that Poe truly loved Virginia and their marriage was a very happy one.

At the *Messenger* Poe increased the circulation tenfold, but the editor Thomas White hated Poe's continual drinking, and fired him in 1837.

From 1837 to 1842, he worked as a freelance writer and editor in New York City and Philadelphia but found it almost impossible to place his work. Those few pieces which were published, like his novel *The Narrative of Arthur Gordon Pym*, earned very little and were totally misinterpreted. In fact, many mistakenly thought *Pym* to be non-fiction. This kind of professional/artistic frustration would continually plague him. Even his best stories, such as "Fall of the House of Usher" (1839), "Murders in the Rue Morgue" (1843), and "The Gold Bug" (1843) sold for no more than 100 dollars each.

In 1839, he moved his family to Philadelphia and worked for a year at *Burton's Gentleman's Magazine* before once again quarreling and getting fired.

His best work, as both a writer and literary critic, was when he was employed at *Graham's Magazine*. He became well known and respected within literary circles. It was one of the only times he wasn't fired. He quit. That was in order to start his own magazine. He almost succeeded, except that when he was supposed to meet with the primary investors, he showed up utterly drunk. His actions also caused him to lose the backing of his most influential and wealthy supporters.

In 1844, Poe moved to New York City. A year later, he published *The Raven and Other Poems*. Finally, he believed he would gain the recognition and financial security he desperately needed, but he was cheated out of the large sums of money the publisher made from the work. The final blow was the death of his wife Virginia from the disease that seemed to haunt the women in his life – tuberculosis. They had so little money that Poe couldn't even heat the freezing cold room where she lay dying. Virginia died on January 30, 1847. Poe became increasingly depressed.

He did rebound somewhat in his final years. He courted several women, lectured, and wrote. In fact, he produced a very complicated and profound book entitled *Eureka*. He also attempted suicide and drank more and more.

In 1849, after leaving friends at a tavern, he disappeared in Baltimore and was found five days later drugged, intoxicated, and near death. Taken to a hospital, he stirred to consciousness one last time and cried out "God help my poor soul!" He died four days later, on October 7, 1849.

Intro to The Tell-Tale Heart, The Black Cat, and The Cask Of Amontillado

Most of you have likely heard of the TV series *Tales From The Crypt*, the *Goosebumps* novels, and probably can name most of the weird, gross-out slasher flicks. On the surface, Poe was writing the same kind of stories in 1843. He created characters (many of them nameless) who murdered innocent people, cut victims up, bricked them into walls, or under floorboards, and heard dead hearts beating.

Three of his best horror stories, "The Tell-Tale Heart," "The Black Cat," and "The Cask of Amontillado," were written in the style of eleven other earlier stories Poe called "Tales from the Folio Club." Poe considered himself an artist, but he also had a very weird sense of humor. These "Folio" stories were all supposed to be a parody, a joke making fun of the amazingly gross books popular with kids in the 1830s and 1840s called *Penny Dreadfuls* and *Penny Bloods* (Essentially that century's *Goosebumps*). The irony was that he was such a good writer, so able to write like a monster or insane murderer – and to go deeper into the minds of these people and make them very human - that the public thought his horror stories were serious. Poe just shrugged, removed the introduction which explained he had written them to mock the gruesome monster and madman stories in the *Penny Dreadfuls*, and sold them to magazines as the real deal (He needed the money).

He explored the kinds of behavior – and the motivations behind the behavior - supposedly never discussed 150 years ago in the Victorian Age, when the "purpose" of "proper" popular literature was to "raise" the standards of morality to a higher level. Poe went in the opposite direction. He didn't want to lower the level of morality. He just wanted us to look at the dark side of our nature, the one he himself peered at daily.

He called it "the inherent perverse nature of all mankind." He didn't mean "perverse" in the modern definition of "perverted," such as the acts of child molesters and sexual deviants. In fact, in most of his work there is little or no physical or sexual contact of any kind. "Perversity" for Poe had a much broader and deeper definition than that. It meant that human beings just can't seem to keep from doing self-destructive, evil things. We sometimes give into our worst nature, our resentments and vengeance; the part that willfully does evil to ourselves and others. It's a big part of our basic mental makeup, what he called "our divided self."

Many authors after him used his original point of view to create their stories and characters. Probably the best known is Robert Louis Stevenson's *Dr. Jekyll and Mr. Hyde* where the good and the bad are literally two people in one body. Oh, and let's not forget werewolves and vampires. As you'll also see, Poe instilled in his characters another element that is part of the secret horror of human nature: the "thrill" of doing evil, the stimulation which comes from the danger they face, the almost electric charge of their unspeakable crimes.

There is a strange kind of hope, a morality, that also weaves its way through the stories. In many cases, Poe's madmen are tortured by guilt. They trip themselves up, returning to the scene of the crime (or never leaving it) and cause their own capture. This is the other element of the perverse: we human beings want to be punished for our sins. Even the ones who get away with it, as Montresor does in "The Cask of Amontillado," are compelled from guilt to repeat the story of the murder he commits over and over for fifty years. This is really important to remember about Poe. As evil, psychotic, and nutso as his characters were or became, they were also tormented by their consciences. They were humans and their personal self-torture was the hell of guilt for their actions.

All in all, it's not a very positive view of human behavior, but one look at the nightly news and it seems that many people and groups have given in to that worst side which Poe was willing to explore. Here, too, is the genius of Poe. We reassure ourselves that his pitiful and desperate humans are fiction. The readers can "watch" from the safety of their armchairs as these monsters and victims meet their fates. We can reaffirm our own positive humanity while acknowledging the monsters we can hopefully keep hidden.

POE'S HORROR STORY TECHNIQUE

Don't be scared off by the word "technique." It's actually one of the most interesting aspects of his writing style. How did he achieve all his creepiness in such short pieces?

The following isn't exactly a list of the secret ingredients of writing great horror stories, but it contains some really interesting things to look for in Poe's creations (as well as things you can try at home!).

For the most part, his characters are nameless but intensely "in your face." When you attach a name to someone, it gives them the start of a very specific identity. Poe didn't want that. He wanted you to be trapped with someone a lot scarier: an anonymous crazy person. The more you wondered who they were, the more you let them burrow into your mind.

He also let you assume and wonder about these characters' motivations. Are they really mad? Were there really terrible insults, past crimes, and anger, or is that just an excuse? Most of the action in his stories takes place at night or darkness, and usually inside spaces, rooms, and caverns which are small and claustrophobic.

He uses sounds, beating hearts, clocks, groaning, and creaking to spook his nameless characters (and you). Sounds are something you can "hear" quite clearly in your imagination.

The characters ask you to consider the possibility that supernatural beings are involved or are responsible for their actions. They never actually admit it. At the same time, they swear to you that they're not mad.

The characters admit that there's that "perverse" sick thrill to their terror or that the same feeling of terrible satisfaction comes from the violent act itself.

And all this in just a few pages. See what else you can discover in his work. Psychopaths haven't changed all that much in 150 years. They can be mentally ill, evil, or perhaps even "possessed." Poe doesn't want you to know what the truth is and what it isn't. He keeps you guessing and that's part of the…fun?

Sit back, make sure there's no one else in the house, and it's dark and the wind is howling, and enjoy the creepy feeling of hearing the story twisted and warped through a maniac's mind. *Just watch your back.*

THE TELL-TALE HEART
1843

Synopsis

A nameless narrator speaks directly to us and so much wants us to believe that he's not mad that it's pretty obvious that he's very, very demented.

He declares his love for his aged employer but is convinced that an unnamed "disease" is responsible for the "sharpening" of his (the narrator's) senses that have made him realize that the old man's "pale blue eye with a film over it" is an evil eye and the old man is out to get him. Therefore, he must kill the old man (more very sick logic).

The narrator waits eight nights, sticking his head into the old man's room each night, until he feels it's the "perfect" time. The night of the murder, the narrator moves slowly into the pitch black room. The old man wakes, and the narrator can hear the old man's terrified, beating heart. He gets concerned that the neighbors will also hear the loud heartbeat. Leaping on the old man – who lets out one horrible scream - he suffocates him with his bedding.

He then dismembers the body and hides it under the floorboards and cleans up the blood till there isn't a trace.

The police come to investigate, called by a neighbor who heard the scream. The narrator states he is at first calm and collected, but the police keep talking to him and soon he starts to hear "a ringing in my ears." This ringing grows louder and louder and soon becomes, to the narrator, the pounding of the old man's still beating heart. Crazed and terrified, tortured by the sound, the narrator tears up the floorboards and shows the police "his hideous heart."

TRUE! — nervous — very, very dreadfully nervous I had been and am! but why WILL you say that I am mad?[1] The disease had sharpened my senses — not destroyed — not dulled them.[2] Above all was the sense of hearing acute. I heard all things in the heaven and in the earth. I heard many things in hell. How, then, am I mad?[3] Hearken! and observe how healthily how calmly I can tell you the whole story.[4]

It is impossible to say how first the idea entered my brain;[5] but once conceived, it haunted me day and night. Object[6] there was none. Passion there was none. I loved the old man. He had never wronged me. He had never given me insult. For his gold I had no desire.[7] I think it was his eye! yes, it was this! He had the eye of a vulture — a pale blue eye, with a film over it.[8] Whenever it fell upon me, my blood ran cold; and so by degrees — very gradually — I made up my mind to take the life of the old man, and thus rid myself of the eye forever.[9]

Now this is the point. You fancy me mad. Madmen know nothing. But you should have seen *me*. You should have seen how wisely I proceeded — with what caution —

1 Whoa. One sentence into his story and this guy is already approaching the on-ramp to Weird City. But notice how starting a story with a word in all CAPITAL LETTERS gets our attention. This guy already is waaaay too intense - and maybe more. . . .

2 A disease *sharpens* his senses? More contradictions.

3 Heard things in Heaven and Hell? Well, that answers the "Will you say I'm mad" question.

4 Calm? Sure. This should be good.

5 Uh, your "disease"?

6 Object - a reason

7 Poe wants the narrator's motives to be stripped down to pure insanity. And notice that he's anonymous. Makes him much scarier.

8 Vultures have blue eyes?

9 An evil eye is almost a totally bogus excuse. *Almost.* Belief in the power of "evil eyes" goes back to ancient times. References to it can be found in many Mediterranean cultures even now.

with what foresight — with what dissimulation[1] I went to work![2]

I was never kinder to the old man than during the whole week before I killed him. And every night, about midnight, I turned the latch of his door and opened it — oh, so gently! And then, when I had made an opening sufficient for my head, I put in a dark lantern, all closed, closed, so that no light shone out, and then I thrust in my head. Oh, you would have laughed to see how cunningly I thrust it in![3] I moved it slowly — very, very slowly, so that I might not disturb the old man's sleep. It took me an hour to place my whole head within the opening so far that I could see him as he lay upon his bed.[4] Ha!—would a madman have been so wise as this? And then, when my head was well in the room, I undid the lantern cautiously — oh, so cautiously — cautiously (for the hinges creaked) — I undid it just so much that a single thin ray fell upon the vulture eye.[5] And this I did for seven long nights — every night just at midnight[6] — but I found the eye always closed; and so it was impossible to do the work; for it was not the old man who vexed me, but his Evil Eye. And every morning, when the day broke, I went boldly into the chamber, and spoke courageously to him, calling him by name in a hearty tone, and inquiring how he had passed the night. So you see he would have been a very profound[7] old man, indeed, to suspect that every night, just at twelve, I looked in upon him while he slept.

Upon the eighth night I was more than usually cautious in opening the door. A watch's minute hand moves more quickly than did mine.[8] Never before that night had I *felt* the extent of my own powers — of my sagacity.[9] I

1 dissimulation - faking it

2 Some deranged killers try to justify their behavior by calling their violent crimes something other than murder. Possibility #2: Remember John Allan, the man who disowned Poe? It wouldn't be the first time revenge was played out in literature.

3 He's getting off on his power trip.

4 Kids, don't try this at home with sleeping parents, especially if they keep a bat by the bed.

5 So, you get that this madman is convincing himself in his *own* mind that the old man's evil, right?

6 midnight - witching hour - Poe uses this in other works. Check out "The Raven."

7 profound - wise

8 Poe uses the character's obsession with watches and controlling time to heighten the relentless push to the story's climax.

9 sagacity - cleverness

could scarcely contain my feelings of triumph. To think that there I was, opening the door, little by little, and he not even to dream of my secret deeds or thoughts. I fairly chuckled at the idea; and perhaps he heard me; for he moved on the bed suddenly, as if startled. Now you may think that I drew back — but no. His room was as black as pitch with the thick darkness (for the shutters were close fastened, through fear of robbers),[1] and so I knew that he could not see the opening of the door, and I kept pushing it on steadily, steadily.

I had my head in, and was about to open the lantern, when my thumb slipped upon the tin fastening, and the old man sprang up in the bed, crying out — "Who's there?"

I kept quite still and said nothing. For a whole hour I did not move a muscle, and in the meantime I did not hear him lie down. He was still sitting up in the bed listening; — just as I have done, night after night, hearkening to the death watches in the wall.[2]

Presently I heard a slight groan, and I knew it was the groan of mortal terror. It was not a groan of pain or of grief — oh, no! — It was the low stifled sound that arises from the bottom of the soul when overcharged with awe. I knew the sound well. Many a night, just at midnight, when all the world slept, it has welled up from my own bosom, deepening, with its dreadful echo, the terrors that distracted me. I say I knew it well. I knew what the old man felt, and pitied him, although I chuckled at heart.[3] I knew that he had been lying awake ever since the first slight noise, when he had turned in the bed. His fears had been ever since growing upon him. He had been trying to fancy them causeless, but could not. He had been saying to himself — "It is nothing but the wind in the chimney — it is only a

1 "Fear of robbers" indicates the dangers of the world.

2 Here he starts to project his own fears onto the old man. Foreshadowing: "death watches in the wall" - the beating heart.

3 So now he both lays his *own* fears onto the old man and *then* disses the guy for having them – Sets the poor old dude up! That's cold.

mouse crossing the floor," or "It is merely a cricket which has made a single chirp." Yes he has been trying to comfort himself with these suppositions; but he had found all in vain.[1] *All in vain*; because Death, in approaching him, had stalked with his black shadow before him, and enveloped the victim.[2] And it was the mournful influence of the unperceived shadow that caused him to feel — although he neither saw nor heard — to *feel* the presence of my head within the room.

When I had waited a long time, very patiently, without hearing him lie down, I resolved to open a little — a very, very little crevice in the lantern. So I opened it — you cannot imagine how stealthily, stealthily — until, at length a single dim ray, like the thread of the spider, shot out from the crevice and fell full upon the vulture eye.

It was open — wide, wide open — and I grew furious as I gazed upon it. I saw it with perfect distinctness — all a dull blue, with a hideous veil over it that chilled the very marrow in my bones; but I could see nothing else of the old man's face or person: for I had directed the ray as if by instinct, precisely upon the damned spot.[3]

And now have I not told you that what you mistake for madness is but over-acuteness of the senses? — now, I say, there came to my ears a low, dull, quick sound, such as a watch makes when enveloped in cotton.[4] I knew *that* sound well too. It was the beating of the old man's heart. It increased my fury, as the beating of a drum stimulates the soldier into courage.[5]

But even yet I refrained and kept still. I scarcely breathed. I held the lantern motionless. I tried how steadily I could maintain the ray upon the eye. Meantime

1 This nutcase doesn't *really* know *any* of this.

2 Any guesses as to which potential murderer now thinks he's 'Mr. Death'?

3 "damned spot" - Poe loved to slip in references to other literature. "Damned spot" most likely refers to Shakespeare's *Macbeth*. A killer going crazy screams, "Out! Out, damned spot!" as they try to wash out a murder victim's blood stains.

4 Back to the tick-tock of time and unstoppable fate.

5 More foreshadowing of the climax.

the hellish tattoo[1] of the heart increased. It grew quicker and quicker, and louder and louder every instant. The old man's terror *must* have been extreme! It grew louder, I say, louder every moment! — do you mark me well? I have told you that I am nervous: so I am.[2] And now at the dead hour of the night, amid the dreadful silence of that old house, so strange a noise as this excited me to uncontrollable terror. Yet, for some minutes longer I refrained and stood still. But the beating grew louder, louder! I thought the heart must burst. And now a new anxiety seized me — the sound would be heard by a neighbor! The old man's hour had come! With a loud yell, I threw open the lantern and leaped into the room. He shrieked once — once only. In an instant I dragged him to the floor, and pulled the heavy bed over him. I then smiled gaily, to find the deed so far done. But, for many minutes, the heart beat on with a muffled sound. This, however, did not vex me; it would not be heard through the wall. At length it ceased. The old man was dead. I removed the bed and examined the corpse. Yes, he was stone, stone dead. I placed my hand upon the heart and held it there many minutes. There was no pulsation. He was stone dead. His eye would trouble me no more.

If still you think me mad,[3] you will think so no longer when I describe the wise precautions I took for the concealment of the body. The night waned, and I worked hastily, but in silence. First of all I dismembered the corpse. I cut off the head and the arms and the legs.[4]

I then took up three planks from the flooring of the chamber, and deposited all between the scantlings. I then replaced the boards so cleverly, so cunningly, that no human eye — not even *his* — could have detected any

1 tattoo - drumbeat

2 The present tense? Is he actually talking to someone or is Poe using the abrupt change in tense to shake up the reader?

3 Riiiight.

4 Oh, now there's a case for insanity. And you thought "Jason" was sick.

thing wrong. There was nothing to wash out — no stain of any kind — no blood-spot whatever.[1] I had been too wary for that. A tub had caught all — ha! ha![2]

When I had made an end of these labors, it was four o'clock — still dark as midnight. As the bell sounded the hour, there came a knocking at the street door. I went down to open it with a light heart, — for what had I *now* to fear? There entered three men, who introduced themselves, with perfect suavity,[3] as officers of the police. A shriek had been heard by a neighbor during the night: suspicion of foul play had been aroused; information had been lodged at the police office, and they (the officers) had been deputed[4] to search the premises. I smiled, — for *what* had I to fear? I bade[5] the gentlemen welcome. The shriek, I said, was my own in a dream. The old man, I mentioned, was absent in the country. I took my visitors all over the house. I bade them search — search *well*. I led them, at length, to *his* chamber. I showed them his treasures, secure, undisturbed. In the enthusiasm of my confidence, I brought chairs into the room, and desired them *here* to rest from their fatigues, while I myself, in the wild audacity of my perfect triumph, placed my own seat upon the very spot beneath which reposed the corpse of the victim.[6]

The officers were satisfied. My *manner* had convinced them.[7] I was singularly at ease. They sat, and while I answered cheerily, they chatted of familiar things. But, ere long, I felt myself getting pale and wished them gone. My head ached, and I fancied a ringing in my ears: but still they sat and still chatted. The ringing became more distinct: it continued and became more distinct: — I talked more freely to get rid of the feeling: but it continued and

1 Macbeth, again.

2 Yeah, but if he was on *CSI* they'd have busted him.

3 suavity - cool

4 deputed - authorized

5 bade - offered

6 So is he crazy enough to *want* to get busted? Answer: Yes. The flip side of the terrible "perversity" Poe felt was in all of us, was the overwhelming shame and guilt, and a desire to be punished.

7 Are we sure, or is he unreliable like he has been throughout the whole story?

gained definitiveness — until at length, I found that the noise was *not* within my ears.[1]

No doubt I now grew *very* pale; but I talked more fluently, and with a heightened voice.[2] Yet the sound increased — and what could I do? It was a *low, dull, quick sound — much such a sound as a watch makes when enveloped in cotton.* I gasped for breath — and yet the officers heard it not. I talked more quickly — more vehemently; but the noise steadily increased. I arose and argued about trifles, in a high key and with violent gesticulations, but the noise steadily increased. Why *would* they not be gone?[3] I paced the floor to and fro with heavy strides, as if excited to fury by the observation of the men — but the noise steadily increased. O God! what *could* I do? I foamed — I raved — I swore! I swung the chair upon which I had been sitting, and grated it upon the boards, but the noise arose over all and continually increased. It grew louder — louder — *louder*! And still the men chatted pleasantly, and smiled.[4] Was it possible they heard not? Almighty God! — no, no! They heard! — they suspected! — they *knew*! — they were making a *mockery* of my horror![5] — this I thought, and this I think.[6] But any thing was better than this agony! Any thing was more tolerable than this derision! I could bear those hypocritical smiles no longer! I felt that I must scream or die! — and now — again! — hark! louder! louder! *louder*! —

"Villains!" I shrieked, "dissemble no more![7] I admit the deed! — tear up the planks! — here, here! — it is the beating of his hideous heart!"[8]

1 No, it was *between* them.

2 Oh, yeah, now that should fool them.

3 Maybe because you're acting like a maniac?

4 Is this really happening or is he *imagining* his own behavior, or the cops' behavior, or everybody's behavior?!?! Whew!

5 Consistent with his earlier delusions of persecution by the old man.

6 Present tense again - who's he telling?

7 dissemble - pretend - but "dissemble" is a very tight word

8 I just get this image of the cops pulling up the floorboards – the old guy is under there looking like he's packed for shipping – no heartbeat. Nothing. Silence. And the killer says, "Oops."

JUST FOR FUN (WELL, MAYBE "FUN" ISN'T EXACTLY THE RIGHT WORD):
You have the role of this insane killer on an episode of *Law and Order*.
Read the story as if you were telling it on the witness stand. Or in the lawyer's office, or to the psychiatrist.

TOTALLY CREEPY: Imagine you are the killer and you're talking to your next victim who's still alive, tied up in front of you, and you're sharpening your machete.

ULTIMATE CREEPY: You're the victim (tied up and still alive for the moment) and you're listening to this madman.

ONE FINAL TWIST: Who says the killer has to be a man?

THE TELL-TALE HEART NOTES

THE BLACK CAT
1843

Synopsis

"The Black Cat" combines elements of both "The Tell-Tale Heart" and "The Cask of Amontillado."

First, we're given a classic Poe psycho murderer who tells you right up front he "did it" and he's being executed the next morning. And then he gives you the rap about not being crazy (sound familiar?), but this guy blames it (first) on the supernatural. So we know he's whack. Well, we're pretty sure he's nuts and lying. Fairly sure. Kinda sure. Well....

Then the story spins in another somewhat unique direction. The condemned madman gives us a sketch of his childhood history. What a great kid he was, how much he loved animals, etc. It's up for grabs whether or not you choose to believe him or decide that it's just the lies of a murdering loon.

The man gets married to a really nice woman, and in a repeat of his childhood, they acquire a lot of animals. One in particular is a loving, very large black cat he names "Pluto."

Things are going great till he starts to drink. And drink. And drink. He strikes his wife, mistreats the animals, and finally, admitting he's given in to the total evil of the demons of alcohol, cuts the cat's eye out as he says out of sheer perversity. Is this enough? Nope. A while later, he hangs the cat from a tree by the neck till it's dead. That night, when a fire burns the house down, they lose everything. But the image of the dead cat is seared into the plaster wall.

His drinking gets worse. And he has to be completely smashed because he brings home another large black cat almost identical to Pluto — right down to the missing eye — except that it has a white mark on its chest. A mark the man is convinced is morphing into the image of the gallows.

He decides that he's got to off this feline as well, but it's no dummy. It won't come within ten feet of him, except on the way down to the basement of a house they're living in. The cat gets beneath his feet on the stairs and almost trips him. He tries to kill it with an ax but his wife stops him. He kills her instead and bricks her up in the wall of the cellar.

The cops show up, find nothing. The man is feeling really cocky, totally cool. He knows he's literally gotten away with murder. He even raps on the wall of the basement; bad career move. A hideous cry and howl comes from behind the wall. When it's torn down, the man discovers that sitting on the head of his very dead and decomposing wife is the black cat that he had bricked into the tomb as well!

FOR the most wild yet most homely narrative which I am about to pen, I neither expect nor solicit belief.[1] Mad indeed would I be to expect it, in a case where my very senses reject their own evidence. Yet, mad am I not — and very surely do I not dream.[2] But to-morrow I die,[3] and to-day I would unburthen[4] my soul.[5] My immediate purpose is to place before the world, plainly, succinctly,[6] and without comment,[7] a series of mere household events.[8] In their consequences, these events have terrified — have tortured — have destroyed me.[9] Yet I will not attempt to expound them. To me, they have presented little but horror — to many they will seem less terrible than *baroques*.[10] Hereafter, perhaps, some intellect may be found which will reduce my phantasm[11] to the common-place — some

1 Another of Poe's play-with-your-head openings, like using "wild" and "homely," which are not your usual adjectives. It kind of puts you off balance. This, on top of the narrator daring you to believe him by saying, "don't believe me."

2 Like "The Tell-Tale Heart" [T3H]. You start to wonder if the narrator's one sandwich short of a picnic.

3 Ouch!

4 unburthen – relieve from burden or trouble

5 Father, forgive me for I have sinned big-time....

6 succinctly - briefly

7 "Without comment"? From Poe? Oh, as if.

8 Well, most accidents do occur in the home . . . .

9 . . .Especially really nasty "accidents."

10 baroques - really gross incidents

11 phantasm - supernatural experience

intellect more calm, more logical, and far less excitable than my own, which will perceive, in the circumstances I detail with awe, nothing more than an ordinary succession of very natural causes and effects.[1]

From my infancy I was noted for the docility and humanity of my disposition. My tenderness of heart was even so conspicuous as to make me the jest of my companions.[2] I was especially fond of animals, and was indulged by my parents with a great variety of pets. With these I spent most of my time, and never was so happy as when feeding and caressing them. This peculiarity of character grew with my growth, and in my manhood, I derived from it one of my principal sources of pleasure. To those who have cherished an affection for a faithful and sagacious[3] dog, I need hardly be at the trouble of explaining the nature or the intensity of the gratification thus derivable. There is something in the unselfish and self-sacrificing love of a brute,[4] which goes directly to the heart of him who has had frequent occasion to test the paltry friendship and gossamer[5] fidelity[6] of mere *Man*.[7]

I married early,[8] and was happy to find in my wife a disposition not uncongenial[9] with my own.[10] Observing my partiality for domestic pets, she lost no opportunity of procuring those of the most agreeable kind. We had birds, gold-fish, a fine dog, rabbits, a small monkey, and a *cat*.[11]

This latter[12] was a remarkably large and beautiful animal, entirely black, and sagacious[13] to an astonishing degree. In speaking of his intelligence, my wife, who at heart was not a little tinctured[14] with superstition, made frequent allusion[15] to the ancient popular notion, which regarded all black cats as witches in disguise. Not that she

1 So, let's get this right: You think the paranormal made you do it?

2 This is like when the neighbors tell the reporter: "But he was such a nice man. . . ."

3 sagacious - smart, clever

4 "beast," but in a nice way

5 gossamer - flimsy

6 fidelity - loyalty

7 So, this guy gets along way better with animals. Hear that warning bell going off?

8 Before he went totally postal?

9 uncongenial - incompatible

10 Or at least the one he was displaying.

11 Here, honey, pet *them* and stay away from *me*.

12 the cat

13 Hey, that's the smart doggie's adjective.

14 tinctured - affected

15 allusion - reference

was ever *serious* upon this point — and I mention the matter at all for no better reason than that it happens, just now, to be remembered.[1]

Pluto — this was the cat's name — was my favorite pet and playmate.[2] I alone fed him, and he attended me wherever I went about the house. It was even with difficulty that I could prevent him from following me through the streets.

Our friendship lasted, in this manner, for several years, during which my general temperament and character — through the instrumentality[3] of the Fiend Intemperance[4] — had (I blush to confess it) experienced a radical alteration for the worse. I grew, day by day, more moody, more irritable, more regardless[5] of the feelings of others. I suffered myself to use intemperate[6] language to my wife. At length, I even offered her personal violence.[7] My pets, of course, were made to feel the change in my disposition. I not only neglected, but ill-used them.[8] For Pluto, however, I still retained sufficient regard to restrain me from maltreating him, as I made no scruple of maltreating the rabbits, the monkey, or even the dog, when, by accident, or through affection, they came in my way.[9] But my disease grew upon me — for what disease is like Alcohol![10] — and at length even Pluto, who was now becoming old, and consequently somewhat peevish[11] — even Pluto began to experience the effects of my ill temper.

One night, returning home, much intoxicated, from one of my haunts about town, I fancied that the cat avoided my presence. I seized him; when, in his fright at my violence, he inflicted a slight wound upon my hand with his teeth. The fury of a demon instantly possessed

1 Riiiight.

2 Yeah, we know: Pluto is Mickey's dog. But did you also know it's the name of the Roman God of the underworld? "Pluto," not "Mickey," jeez.

3 instrumentality - cause

4 Alcoholism, also one of Poe's own problems.

5 regardless - negligent

6 intemperate - angry

7 A "nice" way of saying the weasel hit her.

8 Almost sounds like he's possessed - where's *Buffy* when you need her?

9 In other words, he played "Whack-A-Pet."

10 Listen to the guy, he's right.

11 peevish - disagreeable

me. I knew myself no longer. My original soul seemed, at once, to take its flight from my body; and a more than fiendish malevolence,[1] gin-nurtured, thrilled every fibre of my frame.[2] I took from my waistcoat-pocket a pen-knife, opened it, grasped the poor beast by the throat, and deliberately cut one of its eyes from the socket! I blush, I burn, I shudder, while I pen the damnable atrocity.[3]

When reason returned with the morning — when I had slept off the fumes of the night's debauch[4] — I experienced a sentiment half of horror, half of remorse, for the crime of which I had been guilty; but it was, at best, a feeble and equivocal[5] feeling, and the soul remained untouched.[6] I again plunged into excess, and soon drowned in wine all memory of the deed.

In the meantime the cat slowly recovered. The socket of the lost eye presented, it is true, a frightful appearance,[7] but he no longer appeared to suffer any pain.[8] He went about the house as usual, but, as might be expected, fled in extreme terror at my approach.[9] I had so much of my old heart left, as to be at first grieved by this evident dislike on the part of a creature which had once so loved me. But this feeling soon gave place to irritation.[10] And then came, as if to my final and irrevocable[11] overthrow, the spirit of PERVERSENESS.[12] Of this spirit philosophy takes no account.[13] Yet I am not more sure that my soul lives, than I am that perverseness is one of the primitive impulses of the human heart — one of the indivisible[14] primary faculties, or sentiments, which give direction

1 malevolence - devilish hatred

2 **Time out!**
Warning: Things get gross in the next paragraph – Hey, don't read ahead! – But first think of the word "thrilled" here. Poe gets into it later but a big idea of his was the belief that all humans have a natural inborn capacity to be amazingly cruel (perverse) and that we also, on some level, get off on it. More on this later. **Time in!**

3 Told ya.

4 debauch - drunken disgraceful behavior

5 equivocal - ambiguous, not clear

6 That perversity really starts to kick in.

7 So, that's where cat's eye marbles come from.

8 sez you

9 No kidding.

10 **Time out!**
Next on our tour is a paragraph outlining Poe's views on perverseness. As stated, it's one of the basic beliefs that Poe used as the motivation for the horrible acts of many of his infamous, psycho narrators. Please, keep your hands and feet inside the tour bus at all times because if one of his maniacs is out there they'll cut them off. And they'll do it… Why, class?…Right! Perverseness! **Time in!**

11 irrevocable - unstoppable, can't be taken back

12 PERVERSENESS - meant here as an evil disobedience

13 The narrator [and Poe] feels that the perverseness of human beings was denied and avoided by society.

14 indivisible - can't be removed

to the character of Man.[1] Who has not, a hundred times, found himself committing a vile or a silly action, for no other reason than because he knows he should *not*?[2] Have we not a perpetual inclination, in the teeth[3] of our best judgment, to violate that which is *Law*, merely because we understand it to be such?[4] This spirit of perverseness, I say, came to my final overthrow. It was this unfathomable longing of the soul to *vex*[5] *itself* — to offer violence to its own nature — to do wrong for the wrong's sake only — that urged me to continue and finally to consummate the injury I had inflicted upon the unoffending brute. One morning, in cool blood, I slipped a noose about its neck and hung it to the limb of a tree — hung it with the tears streaming from my eyes, and with the bitterest remorse at my heart — hung it *because* I knew that it had loved me, and *because* I felt it had given me no reason of offence; — hung it *because* I knew that in so doing I was committing a sin — a deadly sin that would so jeopardize my immortal soul as to place it —if such a thing were possible[6] — even beyond the reach of the infinite mercy of the Most Merciful and Most Terrible God.

On the night of the day on which this cruel deed was done, I was aroused from sleep by the cry of fire. The curtains of my bed were in flames. The whole house was blazing. It was with great difficulty that my wife, a servant, and myself, made our escape from the conflagration.[7] The destruction was complete. My entire worldly wealth was swallowed up, and I resigned myself thenceforward to despair.[8]

I am above the weakness of seeking to establish a sequence of cause and effect, between the disaster and the

1 In a way, the concept of Original Sin.

2 Show of hands, class? Uh, parents in the back, you too.

3 teeth - facing

4 Well. . .maybe you do, Sparky.

5 *vex* - annoy

6 Where the narrator says, "if such a thing were possible," what he's implying is that even this horrible act doesn't put his "immortal soul" "beyond the reach of the infinite mercy of...God." He's twisting sin and salvation into a pretzel, but at the bottom he's in terrible pain because of the compulsive actions he can't control.

7 conflagration - fire

8 Oh, as if he was doing a happy dance before the fire.

atrocity.[1] But I am detailing a chain of facts — and wish not to leave even a possible link imperfect. On the day succeeding the fire, I visited the ruins. The walls, with one exception, had fallen in. This exception was found in a compartment wall, not very thick, which stood about the middle of the house, and against which had rested the head of my bed. The plastering had here, in great measure, resisted the action of the fire — a fact which I attributed to its having been recently spread. About this wall a dense crowd were collected, and many persons seemed to be examining a particular portion of it with very minute and eager attention. The words "strange!" "singular!" and other similar expressions, excited my curiosity. I approached and saw, as if graven[2] in *bas-relief*[3] upon the white surface, the figure of a gigantic *cat*. The impression was given with an accuracy truly marvellous. There was a rope about the animal's neck.

When I first beheld this apparition[4] — for I could scarcely regard it as less — my wonder and my terror were extreme. But at length reflection came to my aid. The cat, I remembered, had been hung in a garden adjacent to the house. Upon the alarm of fire, this garden had been immediately filled by the crowd — by some one of whom the animal must have been cut from the tree and thrown, through an open window, into my chamber. This had probably been done with the view of arousing me from sleep. The falling of other walls had compressed the victim of my cruelty into the substance of the freshly-spread plaster; the lime of which, with the flames, and the *ammonia* from the carcass, had then accomplished the portraiture as I saw it.[5]

1 As if to say it wasn't "bad kat karma" that got his house fried.

2 graven - carved
3 *bas-relief* - raised sculpture

4 apparition - phantom

5 Uh, yeah, that's the answer. You're not alone if you can't figure out exactly what happened to the cat and the plaster, etc. But it's actually not important, it's just weird.

Although I thus readily accounted to my reason, if not altogether to my conscience, for the startling fact just detailed, it did not the less fail to make a deep impression upon my fancy.[1] For months I could not rid myself of the phantasm of the cat; and, during this period, there came back into my spirit a half-sentiment that seemed, but was not, remorse. I went so far as to regret the loss of the animal, and to look about me, among the vile haunts which I now habitually frequented, for another pet of the same species, and of somewhat similar appearance, with which to supply its place.[2]

One night as I sat, half stupefied,[3] in a den of more than infamy,[4] my attention was suddenly drawn to some black object, reposing upon the head of one of the immense hogsheads[5] of Gin, or of Rum, which constituted the chief furniture of the apartment. I had been looking steadily at the top of this hogshead for some minutes, and what now caused me surprise was the fact that I had not sooner perceived the object thereupon. I approached it, and touched it with my hand. It was a black cat — a very large one — fully as large as Pluto, and closely resembling him in every respect but one. Pluto had not a white hair upon any portion of his body; but this cat had a large, although indefinite splotch of white, covering nearly the whole region of the breast.

Upon my touching him, he immediately arose, purred loudly, rubbed against my hand, and appeared delighted with my notice. This, then, was the very creature of which I was in search. I at once offered to purchase it of the landlord; but this person made no claim to it — knew nothing of it — had never seen it before.

I continued my caresses, and, when I prepared to go home, the animal evinced a disposition to accompany me. I permitted it to do so, occasionally stooping and patting it as I proceeded. When it reached the house it domesticated itself at once, and became immediately a great favorite with my wife.

For my own part, I soon found a dislike to it arising within me. This was just the reverse of what I had anticipated; but — I know not how or why it was — its evident fondness for myself rather disgusted and annoyed. By slow degrees these feelings of disgust and annoyance rose into the bitterness of hatred. I avoided the creature; a certain sense of shame, and the remembrance of my former deed of cruelty, prevented me from physically abusing it. I did not, for some weeks, strike, or otherwise violently ill use it; but gradually — very gradually — I came to look upon it with unutterable loathing, and to flee silently from its odious presence, as from the breath of a pestilence.[1]

1 pestilence - plague

What added, no doubt, to my hatred of the beast, was the discovery, on the morning after I brought it home, that, like Pluto, it also had been deprived of one of its eyes. This circumstance, however, only endeared it to my wife, who, as I have already said, possessed, in a high degree, that humanity of feeling which had once been my distinguishing trait, and the source of many of my simplest and purest pleasures.[2]

2 Which is why she's been able to put up with you, Chuckles.

With my aversion to this cat, however, its partiality for myself seemed to increase. It followed my footsteps with a pertinacity[3] which it would be difficult to make the reader comprehend. Whenever I sat, it would crouch beneath my chair, or spring upon my knees, covering me

3 pertinacity - determination

with its loathsome caresses. If I arose to walk it would get between my feet and thus nearly throw me down, or, fastening its long and sharp claws in my dress, clamber, in this manner, to my breast.[1] At such times, although I longed to destroy it with a blow, I was yet withheld from so doing, partly by a memory of my former crime, but chiefly — let me confess it at once — by absolute *dread* of the beast.

1 Ow! Ow! Ow!

This dread was not exactly a dread of physical evil — and yet I should be at a loss how otherwise to define it. I am almost ashamed to own — yes, even in this felon's cell, I am almost ashamed to own — that the terror and horror with which the animal inspired me, had been heightened by one of the merest chimeras[2] it would be possible to conceive. My wife had called my attention, more than once, to the character of the mark of white hair, of which I have spoken, and which constituted the sole visible difference between the strange beast and the one I had destroyed. The reader will remember that this mark, although large, had been originally very indefinite; but, by slow degrees — degrees nearly imperceptible, and which for a long time my reason struggled to reject as fanciful — it had, at length, assumed a rigorous distinctness of outline. It was now the representation of an object that I shudder to name — and for this, above all, I loathed, and dreaded, and would have rid myself of the monster *had I dared* — it was now, I say, the image of a hideous — of a ghastly thing — of the GALLOWS! — oh, mournful and terrible engine of Horror and of Crime — of Agony and of Death![3]

2 chimeras - illusions

3 Okay, Let's vote: *Twilight Zone* or *The Freaked-Out-By-Guilt Show*?

And now was I indeed wretched beyond the wretchedness of mere Humanity. And a brute beast — whose fellow I had contemptuously destroyed — a brute beast to work out for me — for me a man, fashioned in the image of the High God — so much of insufferable wo![1] Alas! neither by day nor by night knew I the blessing of Rest any more! During the former the creature left me no moment alone, and in the latter I started hourly from dreams of unutterable fear to find the hot breath of *the thing* upon my face,[2] and its vast weight — an incarnate Night-Mare that I had no power to shake off — incumbent eternally upon my *heart*!

Beneath the pressure of torments such as these the feeble remnant of the good within me succumbed.[3] Evil thoughts became my sole intimates — the darkest and most evil of thoughts. The moodiness of my usual temper increased to hatred of all things and of all mankind: while from the sudden, frequent, and ungovernable outbursts of a fury to which I now blindly abandoned myself, my uncomplaining wife, alas! was the most usual and the most patient of sufferers.[4]

One day she accompanied me, upon some household errand, into the cellar of the old building which our poverty compelled us to inhabit. The cat followed me down the steep stairs, and, nearly throwing me headlong, exasperated me to madness. Uplifting an axe, and forgetting, in my wrath the childish dread which had hitherto stayed my hand, I aimed a blow at the animal, which, of course, would have proved instantly fatal had it descended as I wished. But this blow was arrested by the hand of my wife.[5] Goaded[6] by the interference into a rage

1 "If we could talk with the animals, walk with the animals. . . ."

2 Tuna cat breath, Eeuuwww!

3 succumbed - surrendered

4 We're talking *Lifetime* movie, here.

5 Hy-ya!
6 Goaded - pushed

more than demoniacal, I withdrew my arm from her grasp and buried the axe in her brain. She fell dead upon the spot without a groan.

This hideous murder accomplished,[1] I set myself forthwith, and with entire deliberation, to the task of concealing the body. I knew that I could not remove it from the house, either by day or night, without the risk of being observed by the neighbors. Many projects entered my mind. At one period I thought of cutting the corpse[2] into minute[3] fragments, and destroying them by fire.[4] At another, I resolved to dig a grave for it[5] in the floor of the cellar. Again, I deliberated about casting it in the well in the yard[6] — about packing it in a box, as if merchandise, with the usual arrangements, and so getting a porter to take it from the house.[7] Finally I hit upon what I considered a far better expedient than either of these. I determined to wall it up in the cellar — as the monks of the Middle Ages are recorded to have walled up their victims.[8]

For a purpose such as this the cellar was well adapted. Its walls were loosely constructed, and had lately been plastered throughout with a rough plaster,[9] which the dampness of the atmosphere had prevented from hardening. Moreover, in one of the walls was a projection, caused by a false chimney, or fire-place, that had been filled up and made to resemble the rest of the cellar. I made no doubt that I could readily displace the bricks at this point, insert the corpse, and wall the whole up as before, so that no eye could detect any thing suspicious.

And in this calculation I was not deceived. By means of a crow-bar I easily dislodged the bricks, and, having

1 Why does he use the word "accomplished" if it was an accident? Hmmm….

2 Catch how he's first depersonalized his "wife" into "corpse."

3 minute - tiny

4 Gross Joke #1 - I won't touch.

5 Now she's an "it."

6 Gross Joke #2 - Not going there.

7 Gross Joke #3 – Okay, it would be something about UPS but still, no way.

8 Hey, and then I'll use that idea in "The Cask of Amontillado."

9 Again with the plaster.

carefully deposited the body against the inner wall, I propped it in that position, while with little trouble I re-laid the whole structure as it originally stood. Having procured mortar, sand, and hair,[1] with every possible precaution, I prepared a plaster which could not be distinguished from the old, and with this I very carefully went over the new brick-work. When I had finished, I felt satisfied that all was right. The wall did not present the slightest appearance of having been disturbed. The rubbish on the floor was picked up with the minutest[2] care. I looked around triumphantly, and said to myself — "Here at least, then, my labor has not been in vain."[3]

My next step was to look for the beast which had been the cause of so much wickedness; for I had, at length, firmly resolved to put it to death.[4] Had I been able to meet with it at the moment, there could have been no doubt of its fate; but it appeared that the crafty animal had been alarmed at the violence of my previous anger, and forebore to present itself in my present mood. It is impossible to describe or to imagine the deep, the blissful sense of relief which the absence of the detested creature occasioned in my bosom. It did not make its appearance during the night — and thus for one night, at least, since its introduction into the house, I soundly and tranquilly slept; aye, *slept* even with the burden of murder upon my soul.

The second and the third day passed, and still my tormentor came not. Once again I breathed as a free man. The monster, in terror, had fled the premises for ever! I should behold it no more! My happiness was supreme! The guilt of my dark deed disturbed me but little. Some few inquiries had been made, but these had been readily

1 Used like straw, for a binding agent.

2 minutest - meticulous

3 Yeah, nothing like a little home improvement.

4 This is why cats don't come when you call them.

answered. Even a search had been instituted — but of course nothing was to be discovered. I looked upon my future felicity as secured.[1]

Upon the fourth day of the assassination, a party of the police came, very unexpectedly, into the house, and proceeded again to make rigorous investigation of the premises. Secure, however, in the inscrutability[2] of my place of concealment, I felt no embarrassment whatever. The officers bade me accompany them in their search. They left no nook or corner unexplored. At length, for the third or fourth time, they descended into the cellar. I quivered not in a muscle. My heart beat calmly as that of one who slumbers in innocence. I walked the cellar from end to end. I folded my arms upon my bosom, and roamed easily to and fro. The police were thoroughly satisfied and prepared to depart. The glee at my heart was too strong to be restrained. I burned to say if but one word, by way of triumph, and to render doubly sure their assurance of my guiltlessness.

"Gentlemen," I said at last, as the party ascended the steps, "I delight to have allayed[3] your suspicions. I wish you all health, and a little more courtesy. By the bye, gentlemen, this — this is a very well-constructed house." (in the rabid desire to say something easily, I scarcely knew what I uttered at all), — "I may say an *excellently* well-constructed house. These walls — are you going, gentlemen? — these walls are solidly put together"; and here, through the mere frenzy of bravado,[4] I rapped heavily with a cane which I held in my hand, upon that very portion of the brickwork behind which stood the corpse of the wife of my bosom.

1 Glad to see you were eventually able to get over it, jeez!

2 inscrutability - remoteness

3 allayed - eased, reassured

4 bravado - bragging, pride

But may God shield and deliver me from the fangs of the Arch-Fiend![1] No sooner had the reverberation of my blows sunk into silence, than I was answered by a voice from within the tomb! — by a cry, at first muffled and broken, like the sobbing of a child, and then quickly swelling into one long, loud and continuous scream, utterly anomalous[2] and inhuman — a howl — a wailing shriek, half of horror and half of triumph, such as might have arisen only out of hell, conjointly[3] from the throats of the damned in their agony and of the demons that exult in the damnation.

Of my own thoughts it is folly to speak. Swooning, I staggered to the opposite wall. For one instant the party on the stairs remained motionless through extremity of terror and awe. In the next a dozen stout arms were toiling at the wall. It fell bodily. The corpse, already greatly decayed and clotted with gore, stood erect before the eyes of the spectators. Upon its head, with red extended mouth and solitary eye of fire, sat the hideous beast whose craft[4] had seduced me into murder, and whose informing voice had consigned me to the hangman. I had walled the monster up within the tomb.

1 Yo, Satan.

2 anomalous - freaky, unusual

3 conjointly - together

4 "Craft" as in "Witch. . . .

THE BLACK CAT NOTES

THE BLACK CAT NOTES

THE CASK OF AMONTILLADO
1846

Synopsis

At first, the angry and vengeful narrator is anonymous. All we know is that somebody named "Fortunato" has done "a thousand" nasty things to him, but when he insulted the narrator…well, it's payback time.

The narrator waits till the time is right, and that time is a festival not unlike the wild parties and the street celebrations that take place during Mardi Gras. Fortunato is already sloshed and the narrator lures him down into his ancestral catacombs (tombs) with the lure of tasting a rare and expensive Spanish sherry wine called "Amontillado."

It's here that we learn the narrator's name is "Montresor." Further and further into the depths of the caves they go. Montresor even messes with Fortunato's head, telling him they should turn back because it's too damp and he'll get sick. It makes the drunken Fortunato want to do just the opposite.

Finally they reach a far, far corner of the catacombs and Montresor tricks Fortunato into putting on shackles which are attached to the wall of a recess in the catacomb. Fortunato sobers up enough to realize what's happening and he screams in terror. Montresor screams back, satisfied that the doomed Fortunato will suffer enough to assure the revenge is complete. Then he bricks him into his grave. Now, telling the tale 50 years later, Montresor says "in pace requiescat." Rest in peace.

QUESTION: Who's he really saying that to?

Author's note:

Ever see the ultimate revenge movie, *The Godfather*? Those guys would wait till the time was right and then it was payback time.

Poe knew that revenge is a very destructive emotion. Goes against all the things we've been taught, like forgiveness, talking things out, but Poe explored these kinds of destructive feelings. He was totally tapped into the sleazy qualities of the human beast. He probably would've created *The Jerry Springer Show*. There's even a twist to the usual revenge/murder story at the end of "The Cask of Amontillado." Makes you think.

(Amontillado is a type of very expensive, rare Spanish sherry. pronounced "Ah-mon-till-ah-doh." Or as Homer Simpson would say "Ah-mon-till-ah- D'Oh!")

THE thousand injuries of Fortunato[1] I had borne as I best could, but when he ventured upon insult, I vowed revenge.[2] You, who so well know the nature of my soul, will not suppose, however, that I gave utterance to a threat.[3] At *length* I would be avenged; this was a point definitely, settled — but the very definitiveness with which it was resolved, precluded the idea of risk.[4] I must not only punish, but punish with impunity.[5] A wrong

---

1 "Fortunate" in Italian.

2 "Injuries?" "Insult?" "Revenge?" Once again, Edgar's throwing us smack into the middle of the story. Forget specifics. Don't need 'em. All we need to know, to feel, is the excitement that some dude is going to waste some other dude. Like somebody shouting, "Fight! Fight!" We come running.

This narrator has been pushed too far and this Fortunato character is in his cross hairs. Knowing how ol' Edgar likes to ice his narrator's victims, this foreshadowing of Fortunato is to show he won't be very uh, "fortunato."

3 Oh, Poe is so slick. Like, we're thinking, "Oh, yeah, of course we know who you are…." And Poe knows we'll respond that way. He's given us an "archetypal " character, one that embodies a human emotion we all easily and instantly understand: revenge. Guess what? The instant we recognize it we're hooked again because the narrator, in part, becomes us.

4 The character is going to chill till the time is right.

5 The freedom to mess with this Fortunato any way he wants.

is unredressed[1] when retribution overtakes its redresser.[2] It is equally unredressed when the avenger fails to make himself felt as such to him who has done the wrong.[3]

It must be understood that neither by word nor deed had I given Fortunato cause to doubt my good will.[4] I continued as was my wont,[5] to smile in his face, and he did not perceive that my smile *now* was at the thought of his immolation.[6]

He had a weak point — this Fortunato — although in other regards he was a man to be respected and even feared. He prided himself on his connoisseurship[7] in wine. Few Italians have the true virtuoso[8] spirit.[9] For the most part their enthusiasm is adapted to suit the time and opportunity — to practice imposture[10] upon the British and Austrian *millionaires*. In painting and gemmary[11] Fortunato, like his country men, was a quack[12] — but in the matter of old wines he was sincere. In this respect I did not differ from him materially: I was skilful in the Italian vintages myself, and bought largely whenever I could.

It was about dusk,[13] one evening during the supreme madness of the carnival season,[14] that I encountered my friend. He accosted[15] me with excessive warmth, for he had been drinking much.[16] The man wore motley.[17] He had on a tight-fitting parti-striped dress, and his head was surmounted by the conical cap and bells.[18] I was so pleased to see him, that I thought I should never have done wringing his hand.[19]

I said to him: "My dear Fortunato, you are luckily met. How remarkably well you are looking to-day! But I have received a pipe[20] of what passes for Amontillado, and I have my doubts."

1 unredressed - not taken care of

2 "You gotta stay cool, you gotta stay strong, you gotta stay wiser. . . ."

3 No anonymous water balloons — you have to get in their face — let them know you're the one who's doing the dirty deed.

4 Ever have a "friend" like that?

5 wont - style

6 Sacrifice. . . like a lamb to slaughter.

7 connoisseurship - expertise

8 virtuoso - expert

9 Uh-oh, a little dis on Italians.

10 imposture - faking it

11 gemmary - knowing about gem stones

12 No, not a duck - a phony.

13 In this next part, see if you can figure out why this particular time and place was used by the narrator.

14 The Mardi Gras/Spring Break/Girls Gone Wild type blowouts when everything – *everything* - was permitted that wasn't normally okay.

15 accosted - greeted aggressively

16 Ever have a friend like *that*?

17 He was dressed like a court jester — you know, the "Joker" in a pack of cards.

18 Yeah, good taste is timeless.

19 As in: How ya doin', sucker?!

20 pipe - barrel or cask

"How?" said he. "Amontillado? A pipe? Impossible! And in the middle of the carnival!"

"I have my doubts," I replied;[1] "and I was silly enough to pay the full Amontillado price without consulting you in the matter. You were not to be found, and I was fearful of losing a bargain."

"Amontillado!"

"I have my doubts."[2]

"Amontillado!"

"And I must satisfy them."

"Amontillado!"

"As you are engaged, I am on my way to Luchesi.[3] If any one has a critical turn, it is he. He will tell me — "

"Luchesi cannot tell Amontillado from Sherry."

"And yet some fools will have it that his taste is a match for your own.[4]

"Come, let us go."

"Whither?"[5]

"To your vaults."[6]

"My friend, no; I will not impose upon your good nature. I perceive you have an engagement. Luchesi — "

"I have no engagement; — come."

"My friend, no. It is not the engagement, but the severe cold with which I perceive you are afflicted. The vaults are insufferably damp. They are encrusted with nitre."[7]

"Let us go, nevertheless. The cold is merely nothing. Amontillado! You have been imposed upon.[8] And as for Luchesi, he cannot distinguish Sherry from Amontillado."

Thus speaking, Fortunato possessed himself of my arm. Putting on a mask of black silk,[9] and drawing a

1 He's playin' him.

2 Now he's playing dumb.

3 Means "lucky." Poe enjoyed being sarcastic in naming his characters.

4 Throwing out the bait. . . .

5 Where?

6 …Hooked him!

7 Mineral deposits left behind on stone walls. It can give off a white glow and look really spooky.

8 Fortunato is telling him he's sure the narrator's been taken for a sucker by buying the wine.

9 So he won't be recognized.

roquelaire[1, 2] closely about my person, I suffered him to hurry me to my palazzo.[3]

There were no attendants at home; they had absconded[4] to make merry in honor of the time.[5] I had told them that I should not return until the morning, and had given them explicit orders not to stir from the house. These orders were sufficient, I well knew, to insure their immediate disappearance, one and all, as soon as my back was turned.[6]

I took from their sconces two flambeaux,[7] and giving one to Fortunato, bowed him through several suites of rooms to the archway that led into the vaults.[8] I passed down a long and winding staircase, requesting him to be cautious as he followed. We came at length to the foot of the descent, and stood together upon the damp ground of the catacombs of the Montresors.[9]

The gait of my friend was unsteady, and the bells upon his cap jingled as he strode.

"The pipe?" he said.

"It is farther on," said I; "but observe the white web-work which gleams from these cavern walls."[10]

He turned towards me, and looked into my eyes with two filmy orbs that distilled the rheum of intoxication.

"Nitre?" he asked, at length.

"Nitre," I replied. "How long have you had that cough?"

"Ugh! ugh! ugh! — ugh! ugh! ugh! — ugh! ugh! ugh! — ugh! ugh! ugh! — ugh! ugh! ugh!"[11]

My poor friend found it impossible to reply for many minutes.

"It is nothing," he said, at last.[12]

1 *roquelaire* - a cloak

2 Note: One text accuses Poe of "showing off" by using French words. Probably true.

3 palazzo - home

4 absconded - cut out, split

5 Set up #2.

6 This guy is slick.

7 flambeaux - torches

8 The "vaults" are the catacombs, tombs really, where families would store their wines and, oh, also the remains of every relative who ever died. And some families didn't use coffins. Instead they used the kinds stacked up in holes in the wall. "Hey, let's go visit Great Uncle Horatio!"

9 Let's take a sec with the name "Montresor." Its many meanings can give you an idea of how Poe liked to play games with his readers (who dug it). He used names very sparingly so that when he did he meant to imply several meanings or levels that would enrich the reader who made the effort:
Mont – mountain
In French, "sor" is "fate," and "resoudre" means to determine.
"Mon" - my
"tresor" - treasure
So we have a triple meaning in that it means "to determine my fate (my revenge) is my treasure." How many points do I get?

10 That's the nitre.

11 Not to be too critical, but "Ugh!" Eddy really should've come up with better cough sound effects – You know, like ARRGUH, HACK, COUGH!! GURRHAH! HACK! BLECH!

12 Just love that sit-com timing.

"Come," I said, with decision, "we will go back; your health is precious. You are rich, respected, admired, beloved; you are happy, as once I was.[1] You are a man to be missed. For me it is no matter. We will go back; you will be ill, and I cannot be responsible. Besides, there is Luchesi —"

"Enough," he said; "the cough is a mere nothing; it will not kill me. I shall not die of a cough."

"True — true," I replied; "and, indeed, I had no intention of alarming you unnecessarily — but you should use all proper caution. A draught of this Medoc[2] will defend us from the damps."

Here I knocked off the neck of a bottle which I drew from a long row of its fellows that lay upon the mould.

"Drink," I said, presenting him the wine.

He raised it to his lips with a leer. He paused and nodded to me familiarly, while his bells jingled.

"I drink," he said, "to the buried that repose around us."

"And I to your long life."[3]

He again took my arm, and we proceeded.

"These vaults," he said, "are extensive."

"The Montresors," I replied, "were a great and numerous family."

"I forget your arms."

"A huge human foot d'or,[4] in a field azure;[5] the foot crushes a serpent rampant[6] whose fangs are imbedded in the heel."

"And the motto?"

"Nemo me impune lacessit."[7]

"Good!" he said.

The wine sparkled in his eyes and the bells jingled. My own fancy[8] grew warm with the Medoc. We had passed

1 Catch that "was." He's playing with him.

2 Another wine.

3 Tee hee!

4 d'or - gold

5 azure - blue

6 rampant - whacked

7 "No one hurts me and gets away with it." We have a Sopranos thing going here.

8 fancy - attitude

through walls of piled bones, with casks and puncheons[1] intermingling, into the inmost recesses of the catacombs. I paused again, and this time I made bold to seize Fortunato by an arm above the elbow.

"The nitre!" I said; "see, it increases. It hangs like moss upon the vaults. We are below the river's bed. The drops of moisture trickle among the bones. Come, we will go back ere it is too late. Your cough — "

"It is nothing," he said; "let us go on. But first, another draught of the Medoc."

I broke and reached him a flagon of De Grave.[2] He emptied it at a breath. His eyes flashed with a fierce light. He laughed and threw the bottle upwards with a gesticulation[3] I did not understand.

I looked at him in surprise. He repeated the movement — a grotesque one.

"You do not comprehend?" he said.

"Not I," I replied.

"Then you are not of the brotherhood."

"How?"

"You are not of the masons."[4]

"Yes, yes," I said; "yes, yes."

"You? Impossible! A mason?"

"A mason," I replied.

"A sign," he said.[5]

"It is this," I answered, producing a trowel[6] from beneath the folds of my *roquelaire*.

"You jest," he exclaimed, recoiling a few paces. "But let us proceed to the Amontillado."

"Be it so," I said, replacing the tool beneath the cloak and again offering him my arm. He leaned upon it heavily.

1 Yet another term for small casks for wine.

2 "De Grave" get it? Uh, not too subtle, Eddy baby.

3 gesticulation - hand movement

4 masons - a secret organization of bricklayers

5 Like: "What's the secret password?"

6 A hand tool for applying mortar to bricks — bad joke #2. Mason - bricks . . .get it?

We continued our route in search of the Amontillado. We passed through a range of low arches, descended, passed on, and descending again, arrived at a deep crypt, in which the foulness of the air caused our flambeaux rather to glow than flame.

At the most remote end of the crypt there appeared another less spacious. Its walls had been lined with human remains, piled to the vault overhead, in the fashion of the great catacombs[1] of Paris. Three sides of this interior crypt were still ornamented in this manner.[2] From the fourth the bones had been thrown down, and lay promiscuously[3] upon the earth, forming at one point a mound of some size.[4] Within the wall thus exposed by the displacing of the bones, we perceived a still interior recess, in depth about four feet, in width three, in height six or seven. It seemed to have been constructed for no especial use within itself, but formed merely the interval between two of the colossal supports of the roof of the catacombs, and was backed by one of their circumscribing walls of solid granite.

It was in vain that Fortunato, uplifting his dull torch, endeavoured to pry into the depth of the recess. Its termination the feeble light did not enable us to see.

"Proceed," I said; "herein is the Amontillado. As for Luchesi — "

"He is an ignoramus," interrupted my friend, as he stepped unsteadily forward, while I followed immediately at his heels. In an instant he had reached the extremity of the niche, and finding his progress arrested by the rock, stood stupidly bewildered. A moment more and I had fettered[5] him to the granite. In its surface were two iron

1 "Catacombs" are tombs, not instruments for styling feline fur – Hey! My bad joke #3.

2 Decorated with corpses. Sick joke #1.

3 No, the skeletons weren't doing nasty stuff, it's the other meaning of the word promiscuous: jumbled.

4 Of course, maybe that's what they *were* doing when they all died in that pile.

5 fettered - chained his sorry butt

staples, distant from each other about two feet, horizontally. From one of these depended a short chain, from the other a padlock. Throwing the links about his waist, it was but the work of a few seconds to secure it. He was too much astounded to resist. Withdrawing the key I stepped back from the recess.

"Pass your hand," I said, "over the wall; you cannot help feeling the nitre. Indeed it is *very* damp. Once more let me *implore* you to return. No?[1] Then I must positively leave you. But I must first render you all the little attentions in my power."

"The Amontillado!" ejaculated my friend, not yet recovered from his astonishment.

"True," I replied; "the Amontillado."

As I said these words I busied myself among the pile of bones of which I have before spoken. Throwing them aside, I soon uncovered a quantity of building stone and mortar.[2] With these materials and with the aid of my trowel, I began vigorously to wall up the entrance of the niche.

I had scarcely laid the first tier of the masonry when I discovered that the intoxication of Fortunato had in a great measure worn off. The earliest indication I had of this was a low moaning cry from the depth of the recess. It was *not* the cry of a drunken man. There was then a long and obstinate silence. I laid the second tier, and the third, and the fourth; and then I heard the furious vibrations of the chain. The noise lasted for several minutes, during which, that I might hearken to it with the more satisfaction, I ceased my labors and sat down upon the bones. When at last the clanking subsided, I resumed the trowel, and

1 Now that's just mean.

2 He'd set this all up earlier.

finished without interruption the fifth, the sixth, and the seventh tier. The wall was now nearly upon a level with my breast. I again paused, and holding the flambeaux over the mason-work, threw a few feeble rays upon the figure within.

A succession of loud and shrill screams, bursting suddenly from the throat of the chained form,[1] seemed to thrust me violently back. For a brief moment I hesitated — I trembled. Unsheathing my rapier, I began to grope with it about the recess; but the thought of an instant reassured me. I placed my hand upon the solid fabric of the catacombs, and felt satisfied. I reapproached the wall. I replied to the yells of him who clamored. I re-echoed — I aided — I surpassed them in volume and in strength. I did this, and the clamorer grew still.[2]

It was now midnight, and my task was drawing to a close. I had completed the eighth, the ninth, and the tenth tier. I had finished a portion of the last and the eleventh; there remained but a single stone to be fitted and plastered in.[3] I struggled with its weight; I placed it partially in its destined position. But now there came from out the niche a low laugh that erected the hairs upon my head. It was succeeded by a sad voice, which I had difficulty in recognizing as that of the noble Fortunato. The voice said —

"Ha! ha! ha! — he! he! — a very good joke indeed — an excellent jest. We will have many a rich laugh about it at the palazzo — he! he! he! — over our wine — he! he! he!"

"The Amontillado!" I said.

"He! he! he! — he! he! he! — yes, the Amontillado. But is it not getting late? Will not they be awaiting us at the palazzo, the Lady Fortunato and the rest? Let us be gone."

1 This is subtle but really slick writing: Poe, using the phrase "chained form," is showing us that Montresor no longer sees Fortunato as having an identity. He's just a "form."

2 Screaming with his victim. Oh, man, that's totally sick.

3 "In this episode of *This Old House* Norm will show us how to finish off both a basement and a rival!"

"Yes," I said, "let us be gone."

"For the love of God, Montresor!"

"Yes," I said, "for the love of God!"

But to these words I hearkened in vain for a reply.
I grew impatient. I called aloud;

"Fortunato!"

No answer. I called again;

"Fortunato!"

No answer still. I thrust a torch through the remaining aperture and let it fall within. There came forth in return only a jingling of the bells. My heart grew sick — on account of the dampness of the catacombs.[1] I hastened to make an end of my labor. I forced the last stone into its position; I plastered it up. Against the new masonry I re-erected the old rampart of bones. For the half of a century no mortal has disturbed them.[2] *In pace requiescat!* [3]

1 Maybe…maybe not.

2 He's telling us this 50 years later - he got away with it.

3 May he rest in peace — Yeah, like when they offed enemies in *The Godfather:* "Sorry, it's just business."

The Cask of Amontillado Notes

THE CASK OF AMONTILLADO NOTES

Introduction to The Pit and the Pendulum and The Murders In The Rue Morgue

The Pit and the Pendulum

In some ways "The Pit and the Pendulum" (1842) works as a bridge between "Rue Morgue" (1841) and his three shorter stories "The Tell-Tale Heart," "The Black Cat," and "Cask." (1843 and 1846).

In "Pit," he cuts away a lot of what's called "exposition" or explanations about the characters and their history. He goes right to the action and lets the characters' reactions tell us as much as he wants us to know.

The main character (nameless as usual) seems to be an innocent victim of the Inquisition. He's not the evil one. His torturers are. They're not only anonymous, we don't ever really see them. But they've gone to amazing lengths to enjoy their perverse and vicious acts.

The victim also reacts like a detective as he tries to reason out the shape of his cell and then the ways to escape the multiple ways his unseen executioners want to kill him. These actions take up considerably more time in "Pit" than in the shorter tales, but so many of the techniques – the use of sounds, smells, the nameless characters – sharpened in the three shorter works, are also present here. The vivid descriptions of his discoveries, the near misses, and the visions and thoughts he has brought on by the terror of the unknown (and known), make it read very much like a movie (with a video game not far behind).

In fact, "Pit" has had many film versions produced in many different countries (usually as a symbol of an oppressive government). But like "Rue Morgue" (and unlike the shorter stories), there is a larger amount of commentary on outside issues. In "Rue Morgue," it focuses on opinions about certain types of people, cultures, and later the inadequacies of the police. The observations made in "Pit" cover such things as the brutality and corruption of both political and religious rulers and enforcers (again, the evil nature of human beings). "Pit" can also be viewed as a discussion about the powerlessness of people, and the dangers of a mechanized society as America entered the early phases of the Industrial Revolution. It was a time when human beings would become cogs in the machinery, chewed up and spit out – many times for the enjoyment and profit of those in power (of course that would never happen today).

One other very important difference between this and Poe's later work is the possible salvation of the character, and that this redemption can come in a form or manner far different than we could ever imagine (fortunately, that does happen today).

The Murders In The Rue Morgue

As we've mentioned, Edgar Allan Poe is considered by most the "father" of the modern detective story. The first such story, "The Murders in the Rue Morgue," set the standard for all future writers of detective fiction.

You'll discover in "Rue Morgue" that smart investigative work, scientific analysis, and getting "answers" from the dead didn't start with *CSI*.

Poe's main character in "Rue Morgue," the eccentric and reclusive private detective C. Auguste Dupin, was modeled on a real detective, Eugene Vidocq of the Surete or Paris police bureau (Note: In real life Vidocq was supposed to have been a bit of a liar and blowhard. And in the "real" crime books he wrote, he occasionally exaggerated some facts. Actually, most of them).

Poe's Dupin came from very wealthy parents but lost most of his inheritance and is quite poor (The narrator is also his slightly more financially secure roommate), which adds an eccentricity and mystery to the man. The reader is quick to comprehend that he doesn't try to make a living as an actual detective because he either dislikes the company of most people or can't tolerate their stupidity. Also adding to his quirkiness is the fact that he and the narrator of his stories only go out and walk about at night.

The fictional Dupin gets great delight (in fact, almost his only pleasure) using his powers of reasoning (what Poe calls "ratiocination") to solve crimes.

Like almost all the famous fictional private investigators patterned after him, such as Agatha Christie's Poirot and Sir Arthur Conan Doyle's Sherlock Holmes, Dupin reads everything and retains every fact he hears. Some of the other traits and "rules" which Poe created are that Dupin (and the other fictional super-sleuths) also like to explain all of the details of the investigations to the reader (and the baffled police). He usually prides himself on his intuition, logic, scientific investigation, and creativity in seeing things that either no one else saw or that they saw the "wrong" way. More often than not, he's amusingly disrespectful of the police and their methods and lets them know it. He's entertained by how much it annoys them and, quite honestly, he can be astoundingly conceited to the point of being obnoxious about his abilities. Many of the detectives fashioned after Dupin also have a "buddy" (our narrator again) who is often their only true friend. The bud "tags along," asks the right questions (for our benefit), or is at least told the right answers by the much more intelligent detective.

As a rule the police are either incompetent idiots, well-intentioned idiots, or over-confident idiots. Take your pick: you've seen them all in movies and on TV. The first thing they do when he shows up is either make jokes at his expense or are annoyed that he's there at all. They usually laugh even harder (or are more annoyed) when he makes his first brilliant observation. Note: If the hero or detective is actually on the force, and it's a modern setting, his independent and contemptuous personality also comes from Dupin. Peter Falk's role in *Columbo*, the character played by Bruce Willis in *Die Hard*, Eddie Murphy in *Beverly Hills Cop*, and Mel Gibson in *Lethal Weapon* are examples. They're easily identified (usually at the station house) the minute an idiot detective can't get the soda/snack machine/microwave/computer to correctly work. The hero/detective/rebel always can.

"The Rue Morgue" is what is called a "locked room" mystery. It means that solving the crime seems completely impossible, there was no way for the criminal to commit the crime, and/or no way he/she/it could've escaped. Ah! But our guy, of course, figures it all out, and he's cool, calm, and usually expressionless or with a world-weary smirk.

Poe did reveal his "trick" about how he wrote his detective stories in an article he wrote called "The Philosophy of Composition." That article's discussed in the next section in relation to "The Raven." For our purposes here, the key is that it seems likely Poe did write the detective stories kind of backwards. That is, he came up with the crime and the "who done it and how?" part first, and then went back and built the story to fit.

You'll notice that Poe uses many of the same techniques as in "Pit" and the shorter stories: the action taking place mostly at night, the claustrophobically small rooms, the intensity of the main character, and the vivid descriptions of the violence and the bodies.

So, let's see if you can figure out the crime before Dupin does. Now wouldn't that really tick him off?

THE PIT AND THE PENDULUM
1842

Synopsis

A nameless prisoner is busted for a nameless crime by the whack, nasty judges of the Nazi-like Spanish Inquisition. Their sentencing guidelines are: "One strike, you're dead" (Actually, with these dudes it can just as easily be "No strikes, and if we don't like your 'tude you're also dead). So the prisoner knows he's totally toast. That freaks him out to the point where his mind fries itself, and he goes deaf from shock and starts tripping out on everything he sees and thinks he sees and then quasi-faints and can't tell nothing from nothing.

He's thrown into the slimiest, most pitch-black dungeon ever created. He's so scared he doesn't even want to open his eyes. Big mistake when he does because it's just as dark as if he had them closed. To get his mind off the fact that he doesn't know how his warped torturers are going to ice him (just that they are), he tries to check out the size of the dungeon. He trips over his prison robe and, nose over the edge, finds out they were watching and waiting for him to do a swan dive into The Pit.

Like everybody else in the country, he's heard freaky rumors about this Pit. But nobody believed the government would do something this sicko. They would and they did.

Exhausted, he sleeps. When he wakes, he finds water and bread. He eats and drinks and right before he crashes, realizes they drugged his sorry self.

It's hard to believe that things could get worse, but they do. When he wakes up he's:

A. Flat on his back.

B: Tied flat to a wooden board (except for one free hand that can get to some thirst-causing, highly spiced meat left for him).

C: Has hordes of vicious rats crawl over him and bite him trying to get at his food.

D: Sees that the walls are metal and decorated with totally gross pictures of devils, demons, fiends, and skeletons.

E. Notices that waaay up near the ceiling there's a kind of sculpture of Father Time, only instead of that scythe - the long bladed knife he usually carries - he's toting a very nasty-looking, razor-sharp pendulum. It's swinging back and forth, which isn't scary. But it's coming lower and lower, right at him, which is.

Our bad-luck prisoner's mind bounces back and forth from hope to despair like a super ball till he thinks of a total long shot, no-way-this-is-going-to-work, Hail Mary escape. He rubs the remaining meat on the ropes and lets the rats have an all-you-can-eat buffet. It works! They eat through the bonds, he slides out, and he's FREE! The pendulum goes back up! He's really free! Uh, for about a minute. Those metal walls? They start to heat up like a pizza oven in hell. Remember how he was toast? Well, now he's going to be burnt toast. Can't get worse than this, right? Oh, yes it can. The red hot walls start to close in, obviously trying to push him into The Pit. They come closer and closer...searing his flesh...It's all over...but...WAIT! With only an inch of foothold left he hears voices! And this time they're not in his head! A trumpet blast! The cell walls rush back. Still, he's about to topple into The Pit when a hand reaches down, that of the French General LaSalle. It catches him and pulls him to safety! He and the city have been liberated, saved from the frightful clutches of the Inquisition.

Impia tortorum longas hic turba furores

> [Here the wicked mob, unappeased]

Sanguinis innocui, non satiata, aluit.

> [Long cherished a hatred of innocent blood.][1]

Sospite nunc patria, fracto nunc funeris antro,

> [Now that the fatherland[2] is saved, and the cave of death[3] demolished,]

Mors ubi dira fuit vita salusque patent.

> [Where grim death[4] has been, life and health appear.][5]

**Quatrain composed for the gates
of a market to be erected upon the site
of the Jacobin Club House at Paris.**

1 This is the place where hordes of prejudiced people delighted in the death of innocent victims.

2 fatherland - our country

3 cave of death - the torture chamber

4 Where people were killed by horrible methods.

5 Hope, symbolized by building a market for people.

I WAS sick, — sick unto death with that long agony;[1] and when they at length unbound[2] me, and I was permitted to sit, I felt that my senses were leaving me.[3] The sentence — the dread sentence of death — [4] was the last of distinct accentuation which reached my ears.[5] After that, the sound of the inquisitorial[6] voices seemed merged in one dreamy indeterminate hum.[7, 8] It conveyed to my soul the idea of *revolution*,[9] perhaps from its association in fancy[10] with the burr of a mill-wheel.[11] This only for a brief period, for presently I heard no more. Yet, for a while, I saw — but with how terrible an exaggeration! I saw the lips of the black-robed judges. They appeared to me white[12] — whiter than the sheet upon which I trace these words — and thin even to grotesqueness; thin with the intensity of their expression of firmness — of immovable resolution — [13] of stern contempt of human torture.[14] I saw that the decrees of what to me was Fate[15] were still issuing from those lips. I saw them writhe[16] with a deadly locution.[17] I saw them fashion the syllables of my name;[18] and I shuddered because no sound succeeded.[19] I saw, too, for a few moments of delirious horror,[20] the soft and nearly imperceptible waving of the sable[21] draperies which enwrapped the walls of the apartment: And then my vision fell upon the seven tall candles upon the table.[22] At first they[23] wore the aspect of charity,[24] and seemed white slender angels who would save me;[25] but then, all at once, there came a most deadly nausea over my spirit, and I felt every fibre in my frame thrill[26] as if I had touched the wire of a galvanic[27] battery, while the angel forms

1 Whoa. Already we know that this guy is in a really bad place.

2 "Unbound"? Was he kidnapped? Imprisoned?

3 Check out how he calls them "they." No names. Faceless captors. Purposely creepy. It is the first sign of the uncontrollable power "they" have over him. And no, "they" are not his parents.

4 As bad as a sentence can get.

5 That's the last sound he heard before his mind checked out.

6 "Inquisitorial" has two meanings. One is that at trials they ask questions, but Two – and this is the bad one – has to do with the horrible event called the Inquisition in which our main character seems to have become trapped.

7 He's beyond freaked. Kind of like the way things get fuzzy when you get horrible news or get busted and there's no escape.

8 Poe used sounds, and their absence, as important parts of a story's atmosphere. In some cases they were so important they almost were living things. Poe also liked to mess with readers' heads using clocks, heartbeats, and confusions about time.

9 Lots of meanings: Things, situations revolving, the French Revolution – also going on at the time of the last Inquisition in the 1800s.

10 In his totally freaked imagination.

11 mill-wheel - a big, crushing stone

12 white - bloodless, lifeless, soulless

13 immovable resolution - no way out

14 He knows he's toast.

15 Fate - his death sentence

16 writhe - twist and turn

17 locution - speech

18 Which makes you want to ask, "What is his name?!"

19 He was literally deaf with fear.

20 Poe believed that human beings had something warped going on in their heads that made them crave being scared and in danger. Bungee-jumping, anyone?

21 sable - black

22 No, it's not Kwanzaa or Chanukah.

23 they - the candles

24 Kind of a Kodak moment.

25 Oh, he's way gone.

26 In a bad way.

27 galvanic - electric current

became meaningless spectres,[1] with heads of flame,[2] and I saw that from them there would be no help.[3] And then there stole into my fancy,[4] like a rich musical note, the thought of what sweet rest there must be in the grave.[5] The thought came gently and stealthily,[6] and it seemed long before it attained full appreciation;[7] but just as my spirit came at length properly to feel and entertain it, the figures of the judges vanished, as if magically, from before me; the tall candles sank into nothingness! their flames went out utterly; the blackness of darkness supervened;[8] all sensations appeared swallowed up in a mad rushing descent as of the soul into Hades. Then silence, and stillness, and night were the universe.[9]

I had swooned;[10] but still will not say that all of consciousness was lost. What of it there remained I will not attempt to define, or even to describe; yet all was not lost. In the deepest slumber — no! In delirium — no! In a swoon — no! In death — no![11] Even in the grave all *is not* lost.[12] Else there is no immortality for man.[13] Arousing from the most profound of slumbers, we break the gossamer web of *some* dream.[14] Yet in a second afterward, (so frail may that web have been) we remember not that we have dreamed.[15] In the return to life from the swoon there are two stages: first, that of the sense of mental or spiritual;[16] secondly, that of the sense of physical, existence.[17] It seems probable that if, upon reaching the second stage, we could recall the impressions of the first, we should find these impressions eloquent in memories of the gulf beyond.[18] And that gulf is — what? How at least shall we distinguish its shadows from those of the tomb?[19] But if the impressions of what I have termed the

1 G-g-ghosts, Scooby!!

2 A really subtle foreshadowing — well, it was subtle till I mentioned it.

3 Got that right.

4 Sneaked into my imagination.

5 That's what's called trying to make the best of a bad situation. But seriously, the mystery of the afterlife, of "crossing over"[and coming back] was a main theme in a lot of Poe's writings.

6 stealthily - sneakily

7 Before it was totally understood.

8 supervened - followed

9 What happened?

10 Oh, he keeled over. Not exactly James Bond material.

11 Hey, make up what's left of your mind.

12 Now that's what's called optimism.

13 He's kicking around the idea of "hope" in the form of an afterlife.

14 Check out the importance of dreams and the spirit world in Poe's favorite authors like Shakespeare and Dickens.

15 Yeah, but we still have that drool on the sides of our mouths.

16 Whuh? Did I dream something?

17 Oh, I'm…awake. I'm…here. Whew!

18 We might remember fascinating things – then again, we might remember dreaming that we were late for a test and were running to class naked.

19 Similarities between sleep and death.

first stage are not at will, recalled,[1] yet, after long interval, do they not come unbidden, while we marvel whence they come?[2] He who has never swooned,[3] is not he who finds strange palaces and wildly familiar faces in coals that glow; is not he who beholds floating in mid-air the sad visions that the many may not view; is not he who ponders over the perfume of some novel flower; is not he whose brain grows bewildered with the meaning of some musical cadence which has never before arrested his attention.[4]

Amid frequent and thoughtful endeavors[5] to remember, amid earnest struggles to regather some token of the state of seeming nothingness[6] into which my soul had lapsed, there have been moments when I have dreamed of success;[7] there have been brief, very brief periods when I have conjured up remembrances which the lucid[8] reason of a later epoch[9] assures me could have had reference only to that condition of seeming unconsciousness.[10] These shadows of memory[11] tell, indistinctly, of tall figures that lifted and bore me in silence down — down — still down — till a hideous dizziness oppressed me at the mere idea of the interminableness[12] of the descent. They tell also of a vague horror at my heart, on account of that heart's unnatural stillness. Then comes a sense of sudden motionlessness throughout all things; as if those who bore me (a ghastly train!) had outrun, in their descent, the limits of the limitless, and paused from the wearisomeness of their toil.[13] After this I call to mind flatness and dampness; and then all is *madness* — the madness of a memory which busies itself among forbidden things.[14]

1 If you don't remember that you were running to class naked.

2 Like, you're eating lunch and WHAM! You remember your weird dream! Whew! You're *not* naked.

3 In this next part, he's talking about what this "swooning" personality experiences. In trying to psychologically understand certain personalities he was ahead of his time. Actually, he was ahead of psychology.

4 First, the good side: If you're this type of sensitive person — one who gets overcome with feelings to the point of fainting — you'll experience deep emotions and the visions they cause. The bad part is that, well, you also experience the scary stuff waaaay more than the walking clueless.

5 endeavors - attempts

6 seeming nothingness - apparent unconsciousness

7 Ah, like acing a test without studying.

8 lucid - clear
9 epoch - time period

10 Meaning: He realizes that the only place the good stuff was happening was in the dream.

11 What follows is like a half real/half imagined brain blitz down a whacko Splash Mountain in his skull. Just go with it and enjoy the ride.

12 interminableness - unending nature

13 "Yo, Francisco, I'm beat. Let's sit and chill for a minute. Got a Tic Tac?"

14 "Forbidden things" which are real but which he wants to deny.

Very suddenly there came back to my soul motion and sound — the tumultuous motion of the heart, and, in my ears, the sound of its beating.[1] Then a pause in which all is blank. Then again sound, and motion, and touch — a tingling sensation pervading my frame. Then the mere consciousness of existence, without thought — a condition which lasted long. Then, very suddenly, *thought*, and shuddering terror, and earnest endeavor to comprehend my true state.[2] Then a strong desire to lapse into insensibility.[3] Then a rushing revival of soul and a successful effort to move. And now a full memory of the trial, of the judges, of the sable draperies, of the sentence, of the sickness, of the swoon. Then entire forgetfulness of all that followed; of all that a later day and much earnestness of endeavor have enabled me vaguely to recall.[4]

So far, I had not opened my eyes. I felt that I lay upon my back, unbound. I reached out my hand, and it fell heavily upon something damp and hard.[5] There I suffered[6] it to remain for many minutes, while I strove to imagine where and *what* I could be.[7] I longed, yet dared not, to employ my vision. I dreaded the first glance at objects around me. It was not that I feared to look upon things horrible, but that I grew aghast lest there should be *nothing* to see.[8] At length, with a wild desperation at heart, I quickly unclosed[9] my eyes. My worst thoughts, then, were confirmed.[10] The blackness of eternal night encompassed me.[11] I struggled for breath. The intensity of the darkness seemed to oppress and stifle me. The atmosphere was intolerably close.[12] I still lay quietly, and made effort to exercise my reason. I brought to mind the

1 More sounds! The guy needs a good set of headphones.

2 What was *really* coming down?

3 Well, now that he senses what's "coming down," he wants to leave skid marks on the highway to outta there.

4 Up…down…over…under… wheeeee!!!!…Splash!…AWESOME BRAIN TRIP!!! Oh, sorry. Got carried away inside this guy's freaky jitterbug brain cells.

5 Oh, so that's where I left my pet sea turtle.

6 suffered - forced

7 Hint: It's not Universal Studios.

8 Kind of a "lose-lose" situation.

9 Can't he just say "open"?

10 One of the "lose" situations.

11 *Definite* "lose."

12 One of Poe's favorite terrors he used in order to play with his readers' heads is "Claustrophobia." It's the fear of enclosed spaces, not the fear of Santa, wise guy.

inquisitorial proceedings,[1] and attempted from that point to deduce[2] my real condition. The sentence had passed; and it appeared to me that a very long interval of time had since elapsed. Yet not for a moment did I suppose myself actually dead.[3] Such a supposition,[4] notwithstanding[5] what we read in fiction , is altogether inconsistent with real existence;[6] — but where and in what state was I? The condemned to death, I knew, perished usually at the *autos-da-fé*,[7] and one of these had been held on the very night of the day of my trial. Had I been remanded to my dungeon, to await the next sacrifice,[8] which would not take place for many months? This I at once saw could not be. Victims had been in immediate demand. Moreover, my dungeon, as well as all the condemned cells at Toledo,[9] had stone floors, and light was not altogether excluded.

A fearful idea now suddenly drove the blood in torrents upon my heart,[10] and for a brief period I once more relapsed into insensibility.[11] Upon recovering, I at once started to my feet, trembling convulsively in every fibre. I thrust my arms wildly above and around me in all directions. I felt nothing; yet dreaded to move a step, lest I should be impeded by the walls of a *tomb*.[12] Perspiration burst from every pore, and stood in cold big beads upon my forehead. The agony of suspense grew at length intolerable, and I cautiously moved forward, with my arms extended, and my eyes straining from their sockets in the hope of catching some faint ray of light. I proceeded for many paces; but still all was blackness and vacancy. I breathed more freely. It seemed evident that mine was not, at least, the most hideous of fates.[13]

And now, as I still continued to step cautiously

1 inquisitorial proceedings - the trial

2 deduce - figure out

3 Okay, that's a plus.

4 supposition - assumption

5 notwithstanding - aside from

6 A very tricky way to suck you into feeling that this guy is real. Like when characters in a movie talk about "real life" vs. movies.

7 Not a used car lot. They were the bogus public trials [Remember the opening poem?] where those who believed "differently" than the official religion of the land, Catholicism, were condemned and burned at the stake. Very popular form of entertainment for the general population.

8 Meaning *his* own execution.

9 Spain, not Ohio.

10 Pounding pulse — waiting for that head to explode.

11 Blackout number three!…or four.

12 Buried alive. . .?

13 Oh no?

onward, there came thronging[1] upon my recollection a thousand vague rumors of the horrors of Toledo.[2] Of the dungeons there had been strange things narrated — fables I had always deemed them, — but yet strange, and too ghastly to repeat, save in a whisper.[3] Was I left to perish of starvation in the subterranean world of darkness; or what fate, perhaps even more fearful, awaited me? That the result would be death, and a death of more than customary bitterness, I knew too well the character of my judges to doubt.[4] The mode and the hour were all that occupied or distracted me.[5]

My outstretched hands at length encountered some solid obstruction. It was a wall, seemingly of stone masonry — very smooth, slimy, and cold. I followed it up; stepping with all the careful distrust with which certain antique narratives[6] had inspired me. This process, however, afforded me no means of ascertaining[7] the dimensions of my dungeon, as I might make its circuit and return to the point whence I set out without being aware of the fact, so perfectly uniform seemed the wall. I therefore sought the knife which had been in my pocket when led into the inquisitorial chamber; but it was gone;[8] my clothes had been exchanged for a wrapper of coarse serge.[9] I had thought of forcing the blade in some minute[10] crevice of the masonry, so as to identify my point of departure. The difficulty, nevertheless, was but trivial;[11] although, in the disorder of my fancy,[12] it seemed at first insuperable.[13] I tore a part of the hem from the robe and placed the fragment at full length, and at right angles to the wall.[14] In groping my way around the prison, I could not fail to encounter this rag upon

1 thronging - swarming

2 Hmm…Maybe he *is* talking about Ohio. Just kidding.

3 This place had such a nasty rep that people were afraid to talk about it out loud. Like in *Harry Potter*.

4 He knew that whatever they had in mind, it would be terrible.

5 Let's see, we have an opening to kill you on the twenty-third. Does that work for you?

6 narratives - old stories

7 ascertaining - finding out

8 Gee, what a surprise.

9 A fabric made of rough wool – very stylin' in dungeons.

10 Pronounced: "my-noot" means tiny or small.

11 trivial - insignificant

12 Whacked mental state.

13 insuperable - overwhelming

14 Ah, a little Martha Stewart action.

completing the circuit. So, at least, I thought; but I had not counted upon the extent of the dungeon, or upon my own weakness. The ground was moist and slippery.[1] I staggered onward for some time, when I stumbled and fell. My excessive fatigue induced me to remain prostrate;[2] and sleep soon overtook me as I lay.[3]

Upon awaking, and stretching forth an arm, I found beside me a loaf and a pitcher with water. I was too much exhausted to reflect upon this circumstance,[4] but ate and drank with avidity.[5] Shortly afterward, I resumed my tour around the prison, and with much toil, came at last upon the fragment of the serge. Up to the period when I fell, I had counted fifty-two paces, and, upon resuming my walk, I had counted forty-eight more; — [6] when I arrived at the rag. There were in all, then, a hundred paces; and, admitting two paces to the yard, I presumed the dungeon to be fifty yards in circuit. I had met, however, with many angles in the wall, and thus I could form no guess at the shape of the vault, for vault I could not help supposing it to be.

I had little object — certainly no hope — in these researches; but a vague curiosity prompted me to continue them.[7] Quitting the wall, I resolved to cross the area of the enclosure. At first, I proceeded with extreme caution, for the floor, although seemingly of solid material, was treacherous with slime.[8] At length, however, I took courage, and did not hesitate to step firmly — endeavoring to cross in as direct a line as possible. I had advanced some ten or twelve paces in this manner, when the remnant of the torn hem of my robe became entangled between my legs.[9] I stepped on it, and fell violently on my face.[10]

1 Kind of like the boys' bathroom after a water fight.

2 prostrate - stretched out

3 Kind of like in 5th period after a big lunch.

4 "Hey, anybody order this?"

5 Like he was starving.

6 I thought the math quiz was next.

7 By simply demonstrating this character's curiosity, Poe displays his humanity in the face of brutality. It's a really subtle but powerful way to grab the reader's sympathy for this victim.

8 Also like the boys' bathroom.

9 Whoo-AAA!

In the confusion attending my fall, I did not immediately apprehend a somewhat startling circumstance, which yet, in a few seconds afterward, and while I still lay prostrate, arrested my attention. It was this — my chin rested upon the floor of the prison, but my lips, and the upper portion of my head, although seemingly at a less elevation than the chin, touched nothing. At the same time, my forehead seemed bathed in a clammy vapor, and the peculiar smell of decayed fungus arose to my nostrils.[1] I put forward my arm, and shuddered to find that I had fallen at the very brink of a circular pit, whose extent, of course, I had no means of ascertaining at the moment. Groping about the masonry just below the margin,[2] I succeeded in dislodging a small fragment, and let it fall into the abyss. For many seconds I hearkened to its reverberations[3] as it dashed against the sides of the chasm in its descent; at length, there was a sullen plunge into water, succeeded by loud echoes. At the same moment, there came a sound resembling the quick opening and as rapid closing of a door overhead, while a faint gleam of light flashed suddenly through the gloom, and as suddenly faded away.[4]

I saw clearly the doom which had been prepared for me, and congratulated myself upon the timely accident by which I had escaped. Another step before my fall, and the world had seen me no more and the death just avoided was of that very character which I had regarded as fabulous and frivolous in the tales respecting the Inquisition.[5] To the victims of its tyranny, there was the choice of death with its direst[6] physical agonies, or death with its most hideous moral horrors.[7] I had been reserved for the latter.[8] By long

1 Now this is more like the boys' *locker room*.

2 margin - edge

3 hearkened to its reverberations - listened to its sound

4 Those weasels were watching him! Waiting for him to "accidentally" kill himself. Man, that's cold.

5 All those stories about the twisted freaky ways they kill prisoners were true.

6 direst - worst

7 Well, at least you get a choice.

8 "latter" - the second way — "moral (or mental) horrors."

suffering my nerves had been unstrung, until I trembled at the sound of my own voice, and had become in every respect a fitting subject for the species of torture which awaited me.

Shaking in every limb, I groped my way back to the wall — resolving there to perish rather than risk the terrors of the wells, of which my imagination now pictured many in various position about the dungeon. In other conditions of mind, I might have had courage to end my misery at once, by a plunge into one of these abysses; but now I was the veriest of cowards.[1] Neither could I forget what I had read of these pits — that the *sudden* extinction of life formed no part of their most horrible plan.[2]

Agitation of spirit kept me awake for many long hours, but at length I again slumbered. Upon arousing, I found by my side, as before, a loaf and a pitcher of water. A burning thirst consumed me, and I emptied the vessel at a draught.[3] It must have been drugged; for scarcely had I drunk, before I became irresistibly drowsy. A deep sleep fell upon me — a sleep like that of death. How long it lasted, of course I know not; but when, once again, I unclosed my eyes, the objects around me were visible. By a wild, sulphurous luster,[4] the origin of which I could not at first determine, I was enabled to see the extent and aspect of the prison.

In its size I had been greatly mistaken. The whole circuit of its walls did not exceed twenty-five yards. For some minutes this fact occasioned[5] me a world of vain[6] trouble; vain indeed! for what could be of less importance, under the terrible circumstances which environed[7] me, than the mere dimensions of my dungeon? But my soul took a wild interest in trifles,[8] and I busied myself in

1 Not a modern usage of "very" but an interesting one nonetheless.

2 Then what *did*?

3 at a draught - in one big swallow

4 A chemical glow – Satan and Hell are always linked to the presence of sulfur - seems about right in this place.

5 occasioned - gave

6 vain - unimportant

7 environed - surrounded

8 Unimportant things, like rearranging the deck chairs on the *Titanic*.

endeavors to account for the error I had committed in my measurement. The truth at length flashed upon me. In my first attempt at exploration I had counted fifty-two paces, up to the period when I fell; I must then have been within a pace or two of the fragment of serge; in fact, I had nearly performed the circuit of the vault.[1] I then slept and, upon awaking, I must have returned upon my steps — thus supposing the circuit nearly double what it actually was.[2] My confusion of mind prevented me from observing that I began my tour with the wall to the left, and ended it with the wall to the right.[3]

I had been deceived, too, in respect to the shape of the enclosure. In feeling my way I had found many angles, and thus deduced an idea of great irregularity; so potent is the effect of total darkness upon one arousing from lethargy[4] or sleep! The angles were simply those of a few slight depressions, or niches,[5] at odd intervals. The general shape of the prison was square. What I had taken for masonry seemed now to be iron, or some other metal, in huge plates, whose sutures or joints occasioned[6] the depression. The entire surface of this metallic enclosure was rudely daubed[7] in all the hideous and repulsive devices to which the charnel superstition of the monks has given rise.[8] The figures of fiends in aspects of menace, with skeleton forms, and other more really fearful images, overspread and disfigured the walls.[9] I observed that the outlines of these monstrosities were sufficiently distinct, but that the colours seemed faded and blurred, as if from the effects of a damp atmosphere. I now noticed the floor, too, which was of stone. In the centre yawned the circular pit from whose jaws I had escaped;[10] but it was the only one in the dungeon.

1 Jeez, does it really matter?! Well, it does to *him* because that's *all* he has control over. Poor guy (Pssst…That's what Poe wants you to feel. Ain't he a good writer?).

2 Uh-oh, another math problem.

3 Stand up! Sit Down! Fight Team, Fight!

4 lethargy - inactivity

5 niches - recesses

6 occasioned - caused

7 daubed - painted

8 Kind of sicko graffiti.

9 Happy Halloween?

10 Nice use of metaphors: "yawned" and "jaws."

All this I saw indistinctly and by much effort: for my personal condition had been greatly changed during slumber. I now lay upon my back, and at full length, on a species[1] of low framework of wood. To this I was securely bound by a long strap resembling a surcingle.[2] It passed in many convolutions[3] about my limbs and body, leaving at liberty only my head, and my left arm to such extent, that I could, by dint[4] of much exertion, supply myself with food from an earthen dish which lay by my side on the floor. I saw, to my horror, that the pitcher had been removed. I say to my horror; for I was consumed with intolerable thirst. This thirst it appeared to be the design[5] of my persecutors to stimulate — for the food in the dish was meat pungently[6] seasoned.

Looking upward, I surveyed the ceiling of my prison. It was some thirty or forty feet overhead, and constructed much as the side walls. In one of its panels a very singular figure riveted my whole attention. It was the painted figure of Time[7] as he is commonly represented, save that, in lieu of[8] a scythe,[9] he held what, at a casual glance, I supposed to be the pictured image of a huge pendulum, such as we see on antique clocks. There was something, however, in the appearance of this machine which caused me to regard it more attentively.[10] While I gazed directly upward at it (for its position was immediately over my own) I fancied that I saw it in motion. In an instant afterward the fancy was confirmed.[11] Its sweep was brief, and of course slow. I watched it for some minutes, somewhat in fear, but more in wonder. Wearied at length with observing its dull movement, I turned my eyes upon the other objects in the cell.

1 species - type

2 A heavy twine, also (purposely symbolic) the name of the rope belt a religious monk wears. So it's like he's been "caught" and bound by the Church.

3 convolutions - twists

4 dint - use

5 design - plan

6 pungently - spicily

7 You know, the hooded dude that they always show with the New Year's baby.

8 in lieu of - in place of

9 scythe - knifelike hooked tool

10 In this story, Poe was also making a subtle commentary on the very new and exciting, but also potentially destructive, new age of inventions and machinery that America was just roaring into on its new fangled railroads and steam engines.

11 "Houston, we have movement."

A slight noise attracted my notice, and, looking to the floor, I saw several enormous rats traversing it.[1] They had issued[2] from the well which lay just within view to my right. Even then, while I gazed, they came up in troops, hurriedly, with ravenous eyes, allured by the scent of the meat. From this it required much effort and attention to scare them away.

It might have been half an hour, perhaps, even an hour (for I could take but imperfect note of time), before I again cast my eyes upward. What I then saw confounded and amazed me. The sweep of the pendulum had increased in extent by nearly a yard.[3] As a natural consequence its velocity was also much greater. But what mainly disturbed me was the idea that it had perceptibly *descended*.[4] I now observed — with what horror it is needless to say — that its nether extremity was formed of a crescent of glittering steel, about a foot in length from horn to horn; the horns upward, and the under edge evidently as keen as that of a razor.[5] Like a razor also, it seemed massy and heavy, tapering from the edge into a solid and broad structure above. It was appended to a weighty rod of brass, and the whole *hissed* as it swung through the air.[6]

I could no longer doubt the doom prepared for me by monkish[7] ingenuity in torture. My cognizance of the pit had become known to the inquisitorial agents — *the pit*, whose horrors had been destined for so bold a recusant[8] as myself — *the pit*, typical of hell and regarded by rumor as the Ultima Thule[9] of all their punishments. The plunge into this pit I had avoided by the merest of accidents, and I knew that surprise, or entrapment into torment, formed an important portion of all the grotesquerie[10] of these

1 Must be imported New York City rats.

2 issued - come out

3 Oh-oh.

4 This is also not a good thing to see.

5 For a quick, close shave....

6 Now, there's one of those terrifying sounds.

7 religious jailers

8 recusant - rebellious person – Probably meant as a sarcastic remark because of all the fear he's shown.

9 Ultima Thule - the ultimate

10 weird twistedness – Say, that's a good name for a heavy metal Goth band.

dungeon deaths. Having failed to fall, it was no part of the demon plan to hurl me into the abyss, and thus (there being no alternative) a different and a milder destruction awaited me. Milder! I half smiled in my agony as I thought of such application of such a term.

What boots it[1] to tell of the long, long hours of horror more than mortal, during which I counted the rushing vibrations[2] of the steel! Inch by inch — line by line — with a descent only appreciable at intervals that seemed ages — down and still down it came! Days passed — it might have been that many days passed — ere it swept so closely over me as to fan me with its acrid[3] breath. The odor of the sharp steel forced itself into my nostrils. I prayed — I wearied heaven with my prayer for its more speedy descent.[4] I grew frantically mad, and struggled to force myself upward against the sweep of the fearful scimitar.[5] And then I fell suddenly calm, and lay smiling at the glittering death, as a child at some rare bauble.[6]

There was another interval of utter insensibility;[7] it was brief; for, upon again lapsing into life, there had been no perceptible descent in the pendulum. But it might have been long — for I knew there were demons[8] who took note of my swoon, and who could have arrested the vibration at pleasure.[9] Upon my recovery, too, I felt very — oh! inexpressibly — sick and weak, as if through long inanition.[10] Even amid the agonies of that period, the human nature craved food.[11] With painful effort I outstretched my left arm as far as my bonds permitted, and took possession of the small remnant which had been spared me by the rats. As I put a portion of it within my lips, there rushed to my mind a half-formed thought of joy

1 What purpose is there?

2 Not the good Beach Boys kind.

3 acrid - harsh

4 Kill me! Kill me NOW!!

5 scimitar - big honkin' sword

6 bauble - cheap ornament

7 He fainted again.

8 demons - observers

9 His torturers may have stopped it while he was unconscious so he'd be awake when it sliced him like lunch meat. How considerate of them.

10 inanition - powerlessness

11 At a time like this he's got an appetite?!

— of hope. Yet what business had *I* with hope?[1] It was, as I say, a half-formed thought — man has many such, which are never completed. I felt that it was of joy — of hope; but I felt also that it had perished in its formation. In vain I struggled to perfect — to regain it. Long suffering had nearly annihilated all my ordinary powers of mind. I was an imbecile — an idiot.[2]

The vibration of the pendulum was at right angles to my length. I saw that the crescent was designed to cross the region of the heart. It would fray the serge of my robe — it would return and repeat its operations — again — and again.[3] Notwithstanding its terrifically wide sweep (some thirty feet or more), and the hissing vigor of its descent, sufficient to sunder[4] these very walls of iron, still the fraying of my robe would be all that, for several minutes, it would accomplish. And at this thought I paused. I dared not go further than this reflection. I dwelt upon it with a pertinacity[5] of attention — as if, in so dwelling, I could arrest *here* the descent of the steel.[6] I forced myself to ponder upon the sound of the crescent as it should pass across the garment — upon the peculiar thrilling sensation which the friction of cloth produces on the nerves. I pondered upon all this frivolity until my teeth were on edge.[7]

Down — steadily down it crept. I took a frenzied pleasure in contrasting its downward with its lateral velocity. To the right — to the left — far and wide — with the shriek of a damned spirit! to my heart, with the stealthy pace of the tiger! I alternately laughed and howled, as the one or the other idea grew predominant.[8]

Down — certainly, relentlessly down! It vibrated

1 Good point, Sparky.

2 Maybe Shakespeare again – "Life is a tale told by an idiot, full of sound and fury signifying nothing."

3 Just take a little off the top.

4 sunder - cut

5 pertinacity - focus, determination

6 He's trying to stop it with his mind – Oh, good luck with that.

7 He's starting to lose it again.

8 Oh, yeah, he's totally lost it.

within three inches of my bosom! I struggled violently —
furiously — to free my left arm. This was free only from
the elbow to the hand. I could reach the latter, from the
platter beside me, to my mouth, with great effort, but no
farther. Could I have broken the fastenings above the
elbow, I would have seized and attempted to arrest the
pendulum. I might as well have attempted to arrest an
avalanche!

Down — still unceasingly — still inevitably down! I
gasped and struggled at each vibration. I shrunk
convulsively at its every sweep. My eyes followed its
outward or upward whorls with the eagerness of the most
unmeaning[1] despair; they closed themselves spasmodically
at the descent, although death would have been a relief, oh,
how unspeakable! Still I quivered in every nerve to think
how slight a sinking of the machinery would precipitate
that keen, glistening axe upon my bosom. It was *hope* that
prompted the nerve to quiver — the frame to shrink. It
was *hope* — the hope that triumphs on the rack — that
whispers to the death-condemned even in the dungeons of
the Inquisition.

I saw that some ten or twelve vibrations would bring
the steel in actual contact with my robe, and with this
observation there suddenly came over my spirit all the
keen,[2] collected calmness of despair. For the first time
during many hours — or perhaps days —*I thought.*[3] It
now occurred to me, that the bandage, or surcingle, which
enveloped me, was *unique.* I was tied by no separate cord.
The first stroke of the razor-like crescent athwart[4] any
portion of the band would so detach[5] it that it might be
unwound from my person by means of my left hand. But

1 unmeaning - low life

2 keen - sharp

3 It's amazing what humans can achieve under pressure.

4 athwart - across

5 detach - separate

how fearful, in that case, the proximity of the steel! The result of the slightest struggle, how deadly![1] Was it likely, moreover, that the minions[2] of the torturer had not foreseen and provided for this possibility? Was it probable that the bandage crossed my bosom in the track of the pendulum? Dreading to find my faint and, as it seemed, my last hope frustrated, I so far elevated my head as to obtain a distinct view of my breast. The surcingle enveloped my limbs and body close in all directions — *save in the path of the destroying crescent.*[3]

Scarcely had I dropped my head back into its original position, when there flashed upon my mind what I cannot better describe than as the unformed half of that idea of deliverance to which I have previously alluded,[4] and of which a moiety[5] only floated indeterminately through my brain when I raised food to my burning lips.[6] The whole thought was now present — feeble, scarcely sane, scarcely definite — but still entire.[7] I proceeded at once, with the nervous energy of despair, to attempt its execution.

For many hours the immediate vicinity of the low framework upon which I lay had been literally swarming with rats. They were wild, bold, ravenous — their red eyes glaring upon me as if they waited but for motionlessness on my part to make me their prey. "To what food," I thought, "have they been accustomed in the well?"[8]

They had devoured, in spite of all my efforts to prevent them, all but a small remnant of the contents of the dish. I had fallen into an habitual see-saw or wave of the hand about the platter; and, at length, the unconscious uniformity of the movement deprived it of effect. In their voracity, the vermin frequently fastened their sharp fangs

1 Another lose/lose situation — Free…but sliced into cold cuts.

2 minions - assistants. But also used to describe Satan's followers.

3 Oh, darn. Looks like they thought of everything — Regular Boy Scouts. "Torture" Merit Badges for everybody.

4 alluded - suggested

5 moiety - fraction of

6 Gotta watch those jalapeños.

7 Stop talking and go for it! Jeez!

8 Sounds like they dine on people sushi!

in my fingers.[1] With the particles of the oily and spicy viand which now remained, I thoroughly rubbed the bandage wherever I could reach it; then, raising my hand from the floor, I lay breathlessly still.

At first, the ravenous animals were startled and terrified at the change — at the cessation of movement. They shrank alarmedly back; many sought the well. But this was only for a moment. I had not counted in vain upon their voracity. Observing that I remained without motion, one or two of the boldest leaped upon the framework, and smelt at the surcingle. This seemed the signal for a general rush. Forth from the well they hurried in fresh troops.[2] They clung to the wood — they overran it, and leaped in hundreds upon my person. The measured movement of the pendulum disturbed them not at all. Avoiding its strokes, they busied themselves with the annointed bandage.[3] They pressed — they swarmed upon me in ever accumulating heaps. They writhed upon my throat; their cold lips sought my own;[4] I was half stifled by their thronging pressure; disgust, for which the world has no name, swelled my bosom, and chilled, with heavy clamminess, my heart. Yet one minute, and I felt that the struggle would be over. Plainly I perceived the loosening of the bandage. I knew that in more than one place it must be already severed. With a more than human resolution I lay *still*.

Nor had I erred[5] in my calculations — nor had I endured in vain. I at length felt that I was *free*. The surcingle hung in ribands[6] from my body. But the stroke of the pendulum already pressed upon my bosom. It had divided the serge of the robe. It had cut through the linen beneath. Twice again

1 So if the pendulum doesn't kill him, rabies will.

2 Food fight!!!

3 The one covered in spicy meat juice. Mmmmm.

4 Hey, no.

5 erred - made a mistake

6 ribands - ribbons

it swung, and a sharp sense of pain shot through every nerve.[1] But the moment of escape had arrived. At a wave of my hand my deliverers hurried tumultuously away.[2] With a steady movement — cautious, sidelong, shrinking, and slow — I slid from the embrace of the bandage and beyond the reach of the scimitar. For the moment, at least, I *was free*.[3]

Free! — and in the grasp of the Inquisition![4] I had scarcely stepped from my wooden bed of horror upon the stone floor of the prison, when the motion of the hellish machine ceased, and I beheld it drawn up, by some invisible force, through the ceiling.[5] This was a lesson which I took desperately to heart. My every motion was undoubtedly watched.[6] Free! — I had but escaped death in one form of agony, to be delivered unto worse than death in some other.[7] With that thought I rolled my eyes nervously around on the barriers of iron that hemmed me in. Something unusual — some change which at first, I could not appreciate distinctly — it was obvious, had taken place in the apartment.[8] For many minutes of a dreamy and trembling abstraction,[9] I busied myself in vain, unconnected conjecture. During this period I became aware, for the first time, of the origin of the sulphurous light which illumined[10] the cell. It proceeded from a fissure,[11] about half an inch in width, extending entirely around the prison at the base of the walls, which thus appeared, and were completely separated from the floor. I endeavored, but of course in vain, to look through the aperture.[12]

As I arose from the attempt, the mystery of the alteration in the chamber broke at once upon my understanding. I had observed that, although the outlines of the figures upon the walls were sufficiently distinct, yet

1 Now *that's* gonna leave a mark.

2 hurried tumultuously - hurried and confused

3 That's the good news.

4 That's the bad news.

5 Well, that's our show for tonight! Thanks and please drive safely!

6 You think?

7 Ain't that always the case?

8 apartment - cell

9 Daydreaming, like you do in class.

10 illumined - lighted

11 fissure - gap - No, not the store.

12 aperture - hole - No, not the band.

the colors seemed blurred and indefinite.[1] These colors had now assumed, and were momentarily assuming, a startling and most intense brilliancy, that gave to the spectral and fiendish portraitures an aspect that might have thrilled[2] even firmer nerves than my own. Demon eyes, of a wild and ghastly vivacity, glared upon me in a thousand directions where none had been visible before,[3] and gleamed with the lurid lustre of a fire that I could not force my imagination to regard as unreal.

Unreal![4] — even while I breathed there came to my nostrils the breath of the vapor of heated iron![5] A suffocating odor pervaded the prison! A deeper glow settled each moment in the eyes that glared at my agonies! A richer tint of crimson diffused[6] itself over the pictured horrors of blood. I panted! I gasped for breath! There could be no doubt of the design of my tormenters — oh! most unrelenting![7] oh!, most demoniac of men![8] I shrank from the glowing metal to the centre of the cell. Amid the thought of the fiery destruction that impended, the idea of the coolness of the well came over my soul like balm.[9] I rushed to its deadly brink. I threw my straining vision below. The glare from the enkindled roof illumined its inmost recesses. Yet, for a wild moment, did my spirit refuse to comprehend the meaning of what I saw.[10] At length it forced — it wrestled its way into my soul — it burned itself in upon my shuddering reason.[11] — Oh! for a voice to speak! — oh! horror! — oh! any horror but this! With a shriek, I rushed from the margin, and buried my face in my hands — weeping bitterly.[12]

The heat rapidly increased, and once again I looked up, shuddering as with a fit of the ague.[13] There had been a

1 Kind of like *your* last art project.

2 He means scared.

3 Kind of like the last art project of *The Exorcist.*

4 Totally, dude!

5 Like he's in a really big pizza oven and he's The Meat Lover's Special.

6 diffused - spread

7 They don't give up.

8 Yeah, but they're very creative.

9 You da balm! Actually it means soothing ointment.

10 What?!

11 WHAT?!?!

12 We don't know what he sees down there, but it's worse than being burned to death?…Yikes.

13 ague - fever

second change in the cell — and now the change was obviously in the *form*. As before, it was in vain that I at first endeavored to appreciate or understand what was taking place. But not long was I left in doubt. The inquisitorial vengeance had been hurried by my two-fold escape, and there was to be no more dallying with the King of Terrors.[1] The room had been square. I saw that two of its iron angles were now acute — two, consequently, obtuse.[2] The fearful difference quickly increased with a low rumbling or moaning sound. In an instant the apartment had shifted its form into that of a lozenge.[3] But the alteration stopped not here — I neither hoped nor desired it to stop. I could have clasped the red walls to my bosom as a garment of eternal peace. "Death," I said, "any death but that of the pit!" Fool! might I not have known that *into the pit* it was the object of the burning iron to urge me? Could I resist its glow? or if even that, could I withstand its pressure ? And now, flatter and flatter, grew the lozenge, with a rapidity that left me no time for contemplation. Its centre, and of course its greatest width, came just over the yawning gulf. I shrank back — but the closing walls pressed me resistlessly onward.[4] At length for my seared and writhing body there was no longer an inch of foothold on the firm floor of the prison. I struggled no more, but the agony of my soul found vent in one loud, long, and final scream of despair. I felt that I tottered upon the brink — I averted[5] my eyes —

There was a discordant[6] hum of human voices! There was a loud blast as of many trumpets![7] There was a harsh grating as of a thousand thunders! The fiery walls rushed back! An outstretched arm caught my own as I fell,

1 His jailer was getting totally ticked off with this guy's escapes and wants just to whack him and go to lunch.

2 Geometry at a time like this?!

3 No, not a cough drop. Its shape had been square but now was more of a rectangle.

4 Can't stop da music – or the walls.

5 averted - turned away

6 discordant - clashing

7 He'd hoped for angels, salvation... remember?

fainting, into the abyss. It was that of General Lasalle. The French army had entered Toledo. The Inquisition was in the hands of its enemies.[1]

1 Yea!!! All riiiight! Go team! Kick butt and take names!!!…Phew! Man, that was close.

THE PIT AND THE PENDULUM NOTES

The Pit and the Pendulum Notes

The Murders in the Rue Morgue
1841

Synopsis

The story begins with a lengthy and complicated lecture by the anonymous narrator on the way the analytical mind works. It both prepares and intimidates the reader before meeting the most brilliantly analytical mind Poe can create: His detective, M. Auguste Dupin. We discover that the narrator and Dupin are roommates in a very decrepit, Goth mansion, which they only leave at night.

We are then given a small example of Dupin's deductive powers when he demonstrates how he figures out, literally, what his roommate, the narrator, is thinking.

Reading the newspaper, they learn about the hideous murders of an elderly woman and her daughter. The mother's scalp was half ripped off and her head nearly detached from her neck. The daughter was choked to death and her body stuffed up the chimney.

Visiting the scene, Dupin observes a number of clues. They also read the account of the neighbors and others who heard, but didn't see, the crime. These people were from a number of different countries, and they swore that they heard one male voice speaking a few phrases in French and another voice speaking in a language they didn't understand, but assumed by all the witnesses to be another European tongue.

From this, as well as a strange hair sample in the mother's hand, a nail which looks like it keeps a window tightly closed but does not, as well as other telling signs and clues, Dupin deduces that the murderer's sounds were not a language at all, and the killer was not human.

After finding a ribbon with a knot in it that he identifies as belonging to a Maltese sailor, Dupin places an ad in the paper which reaches the sailor at his address. He deduces that this sailor owned an orangutan that had committed the murders while the sailor watched, helpless to stop the animal. He is, of course, correct, and after solving the case, Dupin explains other facts to the narrator which hadn't before been known.

What song the Syrens [1] sang, or what name Achilles [2] assumed when he hid himself among women, although puzzling questions are not beyond all conjecture. [3]

— SIR THOMAS BROWNE, Urn-Burial.

1 Sirens, the mermaids in the Greek myths.

2 Mythic Greek hero

3 *conjecture* - deduction, figuring out

THE MENTAL features discoursed of as the analytical are, in themselves, but little susceptible of [4] analysis. [5] We appreciate them only in their effects. [6] We know of them, among other things, that they are always to their possessor, [7] when inordinately possessed, [8] a source of the liveliest enjoyment. [9] As the strong man exults [10] in his physical ability, delighting in such exercises as call his muscles into action, [11] so glories the analyst in that moral activity which *disentangles*. [12] He derives pleasure from

4 susceptible of - open to

5 It's hard to figure out how the brain figures things out – got that?

6 We admire the end results.

7 The person who's analyzing.

8 When they're a total brain.

9 Whoopee! I'm playing Frisbee with my mind!

10 exults - delights

11 Yo, check out my abs.

12 *disentangles* - figures out the problem

even the most trivial[1] occupations bringing his talents into play. He is fond of enigmas,[2] of conundrums,[3] hieroglyphics;[4] exhibiting in his solutions of each a degree of *acumen*[5] which appears to the ordinary apprehension[6] preternatural.[7] His results, brought about by the very soul and essence of method, have, in truth, the whole air of intuition.[8]

The faculty of re-solution is possibly much invigorated by mathematical study, and especially by that highest branch of it which, unjustly, and merely on account of its retrograde[9] operations, has been called, as if *par excellence*,[10] analysis. Yet to calculate is not in itself to analyze. A chess-player, for example, does the one, without effort at the other. It follows that the game of chess, in its effects upon mental character, is greatly misunderstood. I am not now writing a treatise,[11] but simply prefacing a somewhat peculiar narrative by observations very much at random; I will, therefore, take occasion to assert that the higher powers of the reflective intellect are more decidedly and more usefully tasked by the unostentatious[12] game of draughts[13] than by all the elaborate frivolity[14] of chess. In this latter,[15] where the pieces have different and *bizarre* motions, with various and variable values, what is only complex, is mistaken (a not unusual error) for what is profound.[16] The *attention*[17] is here called powerfully into play. If it flag for an instant, an oversight is committed, resulting in injury or defeat. The possible moves being not only manifold,[18] but involute,[19] the chances of such oversights are multiplied; and in nine cases out of ten, it is the more concentrative[20] rather than the more acute[21] player who conquers. In draughts, on the contrary, where the moves are *unique* and have but little variation, the

1 trivial - unimportant

2 enigmas - puzzles

3 conundrums - endless problems

4 hieroglyphics - ancient Egyptian (and difficult to translate) writing – kind of like this.

5 *acumen* - skill

6 apprehension - understanding (An unusual use of the word.)

7 preternatural - extraordinary, almost spooky

8 It seems like it's figured it out through some kind of psychic powers but actually figured it out rationally.

9 retrograde - working backwards

10 *par excellence* - the ultimate

11 treatise - extensively written paper

12 unostentatious - ordinary

13 draughts - British term for "Checkers."

14 elaborate frivolity - unnecessary complications

15 chess

16 profound - deep and wise

17 *attention* - concentration

18 manifold - many and diverse

19 involute - unchangeable

20 concentrative - focused

21 acute - smart

probabilities of inadvertence[1] are diminished, and the mere attention being left comparatively unemployed, what advantages are obtained by either party are obtained by superior *acumen*.[2] To be less abstract,[3] Let us suppose a game of draughts where the pieces are reduced to four kings,[4] and where, of course, no oversight is to be expected. It is obvious that here the victory can be decided (the players being at all equal) only by some *recherché*[5] movement, the result of some strong exertion of the intellect. Deprived of ordinary resources, the analyst throws himself into the spirit of his opponent, identifies himself therewith,[6] and not unfrequently sees thus, at a glance, the sole methods (sometimes indeed absurdly simple ones) by which he may seduce into error or hurry into miscalculation.[7]

Whist[8] has long been noted for its influence upon what is termed the calculating power; and men of the highest order of intellect have been known to take an apparently unaccountable delight in it, while eschewing[9] chess as frivolous. Beyond doubt there is nothing of a similar nature so greatly tasking the faculty of analysis. The best chess-player in Christendom[10] *may* be little more than the best player of chess; but proficiency in whist implies capacity for success in all those more important undertakings where mind struggles with mind.[11] When I say proficiency, I mean that perfection in the game which includes a comprehension of *all* the sources whence legitimate advantage may be derived. These are not only manifold, but multiform,[12] and lie frequently among recesses of thought altogether inaccessible to the ordinary understanding. To observe attentively is to remember distinctly; and, so far, the concentrative[13] chess-player will

1 inadvertence - carelessness

2 *acumen* - insight and awareness

3 Finally!

4 Great movie! George Clooney was so cool. Oh, sorry, not the movie, checkers again.

5 *recherché* - researched

6 Ah, he gets into the mind of the person he's playing.

7 Psyche out your opponent.

8 Another name for the card game "Bridge."

9 eschewing - avoiding

10 Hey, you forgot Muslimdom, Jewishdom, Hindudom, and Buddhadom.

11 He's saying card games train you how to handle all kinds of life problems (except maybe how to stop playing cards too much).

12 multiform - many

13 concentrative - concentrating

do very well at whist; while the rules of Hoyle[1] (themselves based upon the mere mechanism of the game) are sufficiently and generally comprehensible. Thus to have a retentive[2] memory, and to proceed by "the book," are points commonly regarded as the sum total of good playing. But it is in matters beyond the limits of mere rule that the skill of the analyst is evinced.[3] He makes, in silence, a host of observations and inferences.[4] So, perhaps, do his companions; and the difference in the extent of the information obtained, lies not so much in the validity of the inference[5] as in the quality of the observation. The necessary knowledge is that of *what* to observe. Our player confines himself not at all;[6] nor, because the game is the object, does he reject deductions from things external to the game.[7] He examines the countenance[8] of his partner, comparing it carefully with that of each of his opponents.[9] He considers the mode of assorting the cards in each hand; often counting trump by trump, and honor by honor,[10] through the glances bestowed by their holders upon each. He notes every variation of face as the play progresses, gathering a fund of thought from the differences in the expression of certainty, of surprise, of triumph, or chagrin. From the manner of gathering up a trick[11] he judges whether the person taking it, can make another in the suit.[12] He recognizes what is played through feint,[13] by the air with which it is thrown upon the table. A casual or inadvertent word; the accidental dropping or turning of a card, with the accompanying anxiety or carelessness in regard to its concealment; the counting of the tricks, with the order of their arrangement; embarrassment, hesitation, eagerness, or trepidation — all afford, to his apparently

1 A book of the rules for card games including Whist.

2 retentive - one that retains info

3 evinced - made clear

4 Silently figuring out your cards by your expressions and actions.

5 inference - conclusion

6 Thinking outside da box.

7 Takes into account things not even specifically connected to the game.

8 countenance - appearance

9 Who's sweating and who's giggling?

10 card combinations

11 trick - played hand

12 No, not clothes, the card suit: Spades, Diamonds, etc.

13 feint - faking

intuitive perception, indications of the true state of affairs.[1] The first two or three rounds having been played, he is in full possession of the contents of each hand, and thenceforward puts down his cards with as absolute a precision of purpose as if the rest of the party had turned outward the faces of their own.

The analytical power should not be confounded with simple ingenuity; for while the analyst is necessarily ingenious, the ingenious man is often remarkably incapable of analysis.[2] The constructive or combining power, by which ingenuity is usually manifested, and which the phrenologists[3] (I believe erroneously) have assigned a separate organ, supposing it a primitive faculty, has been so frequently seen in those whose intellect bordered otherwise upon idiocy, as to have attracted general observation among writers on morals. Between ingenuity and the analytic ability there exists a difference far greater, indeed, than that between the fancy and the imagination, but of a character very strictly analogous.[4] It will be found, in fact, that the ingenious are always fanciful,[5] and the *truly* imaginative never otherwise than analytic.

The narrative which follows will appear to the reader somewhat in the light of a commentary upon the propositions just advanced.[6]

Residing in Paris during the spring and part of the summer of 18—,[7] I there became acquainted with a Monsieur C. Auguste Dupin. This young gentleman was of an excellent, indeed of an illustrious family, but, by a variety of untoward[8] events, had been reduced to such poverty that the energy of his character succumbed beneath it,[9] and he ceased to bestir himself in the world,[10]

1 That's where the expression comes from: "He can read your cards." It means the person can tell what you're thinking by the physical clues you don't even know you're giving off.

2 Too inventive to be analytical.

3 In the 1800s, people who studied the shape and bumps of the skull to determine personality traits – pretty much discredited.

4 analogous - the same

5 dreamers

6 Huh? Oh, we're done with the intro? Great. Let's get on with the story.

7 Pick a year, any year. Actually, what Poe's implying is that the year doesn't matter.

8 untoward - unfavorable

9 Poverty totally bummed him out.

10 Being depressed, he gave up.

or to care for the retrieval of his fortunes. By courtesy of his creditors, there still remained in his possession a small remnant[1] of his patrimony;[2] and, upon the income arising from this, he managed, by means of a rigorous economy,[3] to procure[4] the necessaries of life, without troubling himself about its superfluities.[5] Books, indeed, were his sole luxuries, and in Paris these are easily obtained.

Our first meeting was at an obscure library in the Rue Montmartre, where the accident of our both being in search of the same very rare and very remarkable volume, brought us into closer communion. We saw each other again and again. I was deeply interested in the little family history which he detailed to me with all that candor which a Frenchman indulges whenever mere self is the theme.[6] I was astonished, too, at the vast extent of his reading; and, above all, I felt my soul enkindled[7] within me by the wild fervor, and the vivid freshness of his imagination. Seeking in Paris the objects I then sought, I felt that the society[8] of such a man would be to me a treasure beyond price; and this feeling I frankly confided to him. It was at length arranged that we should live together during my stay in the city; and as my worldly circumstances were somewhat less embarrassed[9] than his own, I was permitted to be at the expense of renting, and furnishing in a style which suited the rather fantastic gloom of our common temper, a time-eaten and grotesque mansion, long deserted through superstitions into which we did not inquire, and tottering to its fall in a retired and desolate portion of the Faubourg St. Germain.[10]

Had the routine of our life at this place been known to the world, we should have been regarded as madmen —

1 remnant - scrap

2 patrimony - inheritance

3 rigorous economy - penny pinching

4 procure - obtain

5 superfluities - extravagances

6 A little dig at the French for being self-centered.

7 enkindled - heated up

8 society - company

9 He had a couple more bucks.

10 Have you noticed how Poe always puts his characters in creepy houses?

although, perhaps, as madmen of a harmless nature. Our seclusion was perfect. We admitted no visitors. Indeed the locality of our retirement had been carefully kept a secret from my own former associates; and it had been many years since Dupin had ceased to know or be known in Paris. We existed within ourselves alone.[1]

It was a freak of fancy in my friend (for what else shall I call it?) to be enamored of the night for her own sake; and into this *bizarrerie*,[2] as into all his others, I quietly fell; giving myself up to his wild whims with a perfect *abandon*.[3] The sable divinity[4] would not herself dwell with us always; but we could counterfeit her presence.[5] At the first dawn of the morning we closed all the massy[6] shutters of our old building; lighted a couple of tapers[7] which, strongly perfumed, threw out only the ghastliest and feeblest of rays. By the aid of these we then busied our souls in dreams — reading, writing, or conversing, until warned by the clock of the advent of the true Darkness.[8] Then we sallied[9] forth into the streets, arm and arm, continuing the topics of the day, or roaming far and wide until a late hour, seeking, amid the wild lights and shadows of the populous city, that infinity of mental excitement which quiet observation can afford.

At such times I could not help remarking and admiring (although from his rich ideality[10] I had been prepared to expect it) a peculiar analytic ability in Dupin. He seemed, too, to take an eager delight in its exercise — if not exactly in its display — and did not hesitate to confess the pleasure thus derived. He boasted to me, with a low chuckling laugh, that most men, in respect to himself, wore windows in their bosoms,[11] and was wont to follow

1 Two intellectuals living in their heads.

2 *bizarrerie* - strange behavior

3 Hey, he digs hanging out after dark. Why not try it?
4 sable divinity - night
5 Turn day into night.

6 massy - large

7 tapers - type of slender candle

8 So, we're talking getting jiggy with the Goth, a vampire thing. Poe put his characters there all the time.
9 sallied - rushed

10 ideality - idealism, philosophy

11 No, not the latest clothing style – It means their real feelings are visible to others.

up such assertions by direct and very startling proofs of his intimate knowledge of my own.[1] His manner at these moments was frigid and abstract; his eyes were vacant in expression; while his voice, usually a rich tenor, rose into a treble which would have sounded petulantly[2] but for the deliberateness and entire distinctness of the enunciation.[3] Observing him in these moods, I often dwelt meditatively upon the old philosophy of the Bi-Part Soul, and amused myself with the fancy of a double Dupin — the creative and the resolvent.[4]

Let it not be supposed, from what I have just said, that I am detailing any mystery, or penning any romance. What I have described in the Frenchman, was merely the result of an excited, or perhaps of a diseased, intelligence,[5] but of the character of his remarks at the periods in question an example will best convey the idea.

We were strolling one night down a long dirty street, in the vicinity of the Palais Royal. Being both, apparently, occupied with thought, neither of us had spoken a syllable for fifteen minutes at least. All at once Dupin broke forth with these words:-

"He is a very little fellow, that's true, and would do better for the *Théâtre des Variétés*."[6]

"There can be no doubt of that," I replied, unwittingly,[7] and not at first observing (so much had I been absorbed in reflection) the extraordinary manner in which the speaker[8] had chimed in with my meditations. In an instant afterward I recollected myself, and my astonishment was profound.[9]

"Dupin," said I, gravely, "this is beyond my comprehension. I do not hesitate to say that I am amazed,

1 He could "read the narrator's cards."

2 petulantly - irritably

3 enunciation - speaking

4 resolvent - focused and determined

5 Once again, Poe gives us negative choices to define the mood and perhaps, but not always, the character.

6 Parisian Vaudeville/Comedy Theater

7 unwittingly - involuntarily

8 Dupin

9 Hey, how'd he do that?!

and can scarcely credit my senses. How was it possible you should know I was thinking of — ?" Here I paused, to ascertain beyond a doubt whether he really knew of whom I thought.

"—— of Chantilly," said he, "why do you pause? You were remarking to yourself that his diminutive[1] figure unfitted him for tragedy."

This was precisely what had formed the subject of my reflections. Chantilly was a quondam[2] cobbler of the Rue St. Denis, who, becoming stage-mad, had attempted the rôle of Xerxes, in Crébillon's tragedy[3] so called, and been notoriously Pasquinaded for his pains.[4]

"Tell me, for Heaven's sake," I exclaimed, "the method — if method there is — by which you have been enabled to fathom[5] my soul in this matter." In fact, I was even more startled than I would have been willing to express.

"It was the fruiterer,"[6] replied my friend, "who brought you to the conclusion that the mender of soles[7] was not of sufficient height for Xerxes *et id genus omne*."[8]

"The fruiterer! — you astonish me — I know no fruiterer whomsoever."

"The man who ran up against you as we entered the street — it may have been fifteen minutes ago."

I now remembered that, in fact, a fruiterer, carrying upon his head a large basket of apples, had nearly thrown me down, by accident, as we passed from the Rue C— into the thoroughfare where we stood; but what this had to do with Chantilly I could not possibly understand.

There was not a particle of *charlatanerie*[9] about Dupin. "I will explain," he said, "and that you may comprehend all clearly, we will explain," he said, "and that

1 diminutive - slight, small

2 quondam - former

3 play

4 Pasquinaded – A tradition started in 1501 when people would write criticisms dissing someone and post them, originally on an old Roman statue, later on a public bulletin board. These days they just trash your locker.

5 fathom - understand

6 Say that three times fast. Actually it's a person who sells fruit – duh.

7 Cobbler = shoe repair; soles = souls. Get it? Baaad.

8 Types of that specific classification – of characters, in this case

9 *charlatanerie* - phoniness

you may comprehend all clearly, we will first retrace the course of your meditations, from the moment in which I spoke to you until that of the *rencontre*[1] with the fruiterer in question. The larger links of the chain run thus — Chantilly, Orion, Dr. Nichols, Epicurus, Stereotomy, the street stones, the fruiterer."[2]

1 *rencontre* - encounter

2 These are the main points by which Dupin was able to figure out what the narrator was thinking.

There are few persons who have not, at some period of their lives, amused themselves in retracing their steps by which particular conclusions of their own minds have been attained.[3] The occupation is often full of interest; and he who attempts it for the first time is astonished by the apparently illimitable[4] distance and incoherence[5] between the starting-point and the goal.[6] What, then, must have been my amazement, when I heard the Frenchman speak what he had just spoken, and when I could not help acknowledging that he had spoken the truth. He continued:

3 Like when you're waiting in line to renew your driver's license.

4 illimitable - unlimited

5 incoherence - irrationality

6 Hey, how did I get in line?

"We had been talking of horses, if I remember aright, just before leaving the Rue C—. This was the last subject we discussed. As we crossed into this street, a fruiterer, with a large basket upon his head, brushing quickly past us, thrust you upon a pile of paving-stones collected at a spot where the causeway[7] is undergoing repair. You stepped upon one of the loose fragments, slipped, slightly strained your ankle, appeared vexed[8] or sulky, muttered a few words,[9] turned to look at the pile, and then proceeded in silence. I was not particularly attentive to what you did; but observation has become with me, of late, a species of necessity. [10]

7 causeway - street

8 vexed - annoyed

9 !@#%!!#

10 He just can't help himself.

"You kept your eyes upon the ground — glancing, with a petulant[11] expression, at the holes and ruts in the

11 petulant - grumpy

pavement, (so that I saw you were still thinking of the stones,)[1] until we reached the little alley called Lamartine, which has been paved, by way of experiment, with the overlapping and riveted blocks. Here your countenance brightened up, and, perceiving your lips move, I could not doubt that you murmured the word 'stereotomy,'[2] a term very affectedly applied to this species of pavement.[3] I knew that you could not say to yourself 'stereotomy' without being brought to think of atomies,[4] and thus of the theories of Epicurus;[5] and since, when we discussed this subject not very long ago, I mentioned to you how singularly, yet with how little notice, the vague guesses of that noble Greek had met with confirmation in the late nebular cosmogony,[6] I felt that you could not avoid casting your eyes upward to the great *nebula* in Orion, and I certainly expected that you would do so. You did look up; and I was now assured that I had correctly followed your steps. But in that bitter *tirade* upon Chantilly, which appeared in yesterday's '*Musee*,' the satirist, making some disgraceful allusions to the cobbler's change of name upon assuming the buskin,[7] quoted a Latin line about which we have often conversed. I mean the line

Perdidit antiquum litera prima sonum.

I had told you that this was in reference to Orion, formerly written Urion; and, from certain pungencies[8] connected with this explanation, I was aware that you could not have forgotten it. It was clear, therefore, that you would not fail to combine the two ideas of Orion and Chantilly. That you did combine them I say by the character of the smile which passed over your lips. You thought of the poor cobbler's immolation.[9] So far, you had been stooping in

1 There will be no bad Mick Jagger jokes in this spot. But only because we couldn't think of one.

2 'stereotomy - the art of cutting stone

3 Glad *he* knew what it meant.

4 atomies - study of the heavens

5 He put forward a theory of the universe that was based on atoms moving about in random patterns and who also believed that God existed but didn't care about humans.

6 cosmogony - study of the composition of the universe

7 Symbolic costume of a traveling entertainer. Kind of meant as a put down.

8 Acid - nasty put down.

9 The critics fried him.

your gait; but now I saw you draw yourself up to your full height. I was then sure that you reflected upon the diminutive figure of Chantilly. At this point I interrupted your meditations to remark that as, in fact, he *was* a very little fellow — that Chantilly — he would do better at the *Theatre des Varietes*."

Not long after this, we were looking over an evening edition of the "*Gazette des Tribunaux*," when the following paragraphs arrested our attention.

"EXTRAORDINARY MURDERS. — This morning, about three o'clock, the inhabitants of the Quartier St. Roch were aroused from sleep by a succession of terrific shrieks, issuing, apparently, from the fourth story of a house in the Rue Morgue, known to be in the sole occupancy of one Madame L'Espanaye, and her daughter, Mademoiselle Camille L'Espanaye. After some delay, occasioned by a fruitless attempt to procure admission in the usual manner, the gateway was broken in with a crowbar, and eight or ten of the neighbors entered, accompanied by two *gendarmes*. By this time the cries had ceased; but, as the party rushed up the first flight of stairs, two or more rough voices, in angry contention, were distinguished, and seemed to proceed from the upper part of the house. As the second landing was reached, these sounds, also, had ceased, and every thing remained perfectly quiet. The party spread themselves, and hurried from room to room. Upon arriving at a large back chamber in the fourth story, (the door of which, being found locked, with the key inside, was forced open,) a spectacle presented itself which struck every one present not less with horror than with astonishment.

"The apartment was in the wildest disorder — the

furniture broken and thrown about in all directions. There was only one bedstead; and from this the bed had been removed, and thrown into the middle of the floor. On a chair lay a razor, besmeared with blood. On the hearth were two or three long and thick tresses of grey human hair, also dabbled in blood, and seeming to have been pulled out by the roots. On the floor were found four Napoleons,[1] an ear-ring of topaz, three large silver spoons, three smaller of *metal d'Alger*, and two bags, containing nearly four thousand francs in gold. The drawers of a *bureau*, which stood in one corner, were open, and had been, apparently, rifled,[2] although many articles still remained in them. A small iron safe was discovered under the *bed* (not under the bedstead).[3] It was open, with the key still in the door. It had no contents beyond a few old letters, and other papers of little consequence.[4]

"Of Madame L'Espanaye no traces were here seen; but an unusual quantity of soot being observed in the fire-place, a search was made in the chimney, and (horrible to relate!) the corpse of the daughter, head downward, was dragged therefrom; it having been thus forced up the narrow aperture for a considerable distance. The body was quite warm. Upon examining it, many excoriations[5] were perceived, no doubt occasioned by the violence with which it had been thrust up and disengaged.[6] Upon the face were many severe scratches, and, upon the throat, dark bruises, and deep indentations of finger nails, as if the deceased had been throttled to death.

"After a thorough investigation of every portion of the house without farther discovery, the party made its way into a small paved yard in the rear of the building,

1 Not little dictators, but gold coins.

2 rifled - looted

3 bedstead - couch

4 First guess: Parents went out, kids had a party. Okay, maybe.

5 excoriations - cuts and bruises

6 disengaged - pulled out

where lay the corpse of the old lady, with her throat so entirely cut that, upon an attempt to raise her, the head fell off. The body, as well as the head, was fearfully mutilated — the former so much so as scarcely to retain any semblance of humanity.[1]

"To this horrible mystery there is not as yet, we believe, the slightest clew."[2]

The next day's paper had these additional particulars.

"*The Tragedy in the Rue Morgue.* — Many individuals have been examined in relation to this most extraordinary and frightful affair," [The word *'affaire'* has not yet, in France, that levity[3] of import which it conveys with us] "but nothing whatever has transpired to throw light upon We give below all the material testimony elicited.[4]

"*Pauline Dubourg*, laundress, deposes[5] that she has known both the deceased for three years, having washed for them during that period. The old lady and her daughter seemed on good terms — very affectionate toward each other. They were excellent pay.[6] Could not speak in regard to their mode or means of living. Believed that Madame L. told fortunes for a living.[7] Was reputed[8] to have money put by.[9] Never met any person in the house when she called for the clothes or took them home. Was sure that they had no servant in employ. There appeared to be no furniture in any part of the building except in the fourth story.

"*Pierre Moreau*, tobacconist, deposes that he has been in the habit of selling small quantities of tobacco and snuff to Madame L'Espanaye for nearly four years.[10] Was born in the neighborhood, and has always resided there. The deceased and her daughter had occupied the house in

1 And you thought the O.J. Simpson case was nasty.

2 Is that true?

3 levity - light, humorous

4 Here, in the form of the police reports, is the puzzle Dupin's faced with.

5 deposes -makes an official statement to officials

6 excellent pay - paid well

7 Another touch of the supernatural.

8 reputed - believed, or assumed

9 money put by - saved

10 Wonder if she liked Skol or Red Man?

which the corpses were found, for more than six years. It was formerly occupied by a jeweller, who under-let the upper rooms to various persons. The house was the property of Madame L. She became dissatisfied with the abuse of the premises by her tenant, and moved into them herself, refusing to let any portion. The old lady was childish. Witness had seen the daughter some five or six times during the six years. The two lived an exceedingly retired life — were reputed to have money. Had heard it said among the neighbors that Madame L. told fortunes — did not believe it. Had never seen any person enter the door except the old lady and her daughter, a porter once or twice, and a physician some eight or ten times.

"Many other persons, neighbors, gave evidence to the same effect.[1] No one was spoken of as frequenting the house. It was not known whether there were any living connections of Madame L. and her daughter. The shutters of the front windows were seldom opened.[2] Those in the rear were always closed, with the exception of the large back room, fourth story. The house was a good house — not very old.

"*Isidore Muset, gendarme,*[3] deposes that he was called to the house about three o'clock in the morning, and found some twenty or thirty persons at the gateway, endeavoring to gain admittance. Forced it open, at length, with a bayonet — not with a crowbar. Had but little difficulty in getting it open, on account of its being a double or folding gate, and bolted neither at bottom nor top. The shrieks were continued until the gate was forced — and then suddenly ceased. They seemed to be screams of some person (or persons) in great agony — were loud and drawn

1 to the same effect - said the same thing

2 That's also how our two guys live. Hmmm....

3 *gendarme* - police officer

out, not short and quick. Witness led the way up stairs. Upon reaching the first landing, heard two voices in loud and angry contention — the one a gruff voice, the other much shriller — a very strange voice. Could distinguish some words of the former, which was that of a Frenchman. Was positive that it was not a woman's voice. Could distinguish the words '*sacre*'[1] and '*diable*.'[2] The shrill voice was that of a foreigner. Could not be sure whether it was the voice of a man or of a woman. Could not make out what was said, but believed the language to be Spanish. The state of the room and of the bodies was described by this witness as we described them yesterday.[3]

"*Henri Duval*, a neighbor, and by trade a silver-smith, deposes that he was one of the party who first entered the house. Corroborates[4] the testimony of Musèt in general. As soon as they forced an entrance, they reclosed the door, to keep out the crowd, which collected very fast, notwithstanding the lateness of the hour. The shrill voice, the witness thinks, was that of an Italian. Was certain it was not French. Could not be sure that it was a man's voice. It might have been a woman's. Was not acquainted with the Italian language. Could not distinguish the words, but was convinced by the intonation that the speaker was an Italian. Knew Madame L. and her daughter. Had conversed with both frequently. Was sure that the shrill voice was not that of either of the deceased.

"——*Odenheimer, restaurateur*— This witness volunteered his testimony. Not speaking French, was examined through an interpreter. Is a native of Amsterdam. Was passing the house at the time of the shrieks. They lasted for several minutes — probably ten. They were long and loud — very

1 *sacre* - sacred
2 *diable* - devil

3 Doesn't this beginning sound a lot like the way they investigate on *Law and Order*?

4 Corroborates - confirms

awful and distressing. Was one of those who entered the building. Corroborated the previous evidence in every respect but one. Was sure that the shrill voice was that of a man — of a Frenchman. Could not distinguish the words uttered. They were loud and quick — unequal — spoken apparently in fear as well as in anger. The voice was harsh — not so much shrill as harsh. Could not call it a shrill voice. The gruff voice said repeatedly '*sacre*,' '*diable*' and once '*mon Dieu*.'[1]

1 *mon Dieu* - My God!

"*Jules Mignaud*, banker, of the firm of Mignaud et Fils,[2] Rue Deloraine. Is the elder Mignaud. Madame L'Espanaye had some property. Had opened an account with his baking house in the spring of the year — (eight years previously). Made frequent deposits in small sums. Had checked for nothing until the third day before her death, when she took out in person the sum of 4000 francs. This sum was paid in gold, and a clerk sent home with the money.

2 et Fils - and Sons

"*Adolphe Le Bon*, clerk to Mignaud et Fils, deposes that on the day in question, about noon, he accompanied Madame L'Espanaye to her residence with the 4000 francs, put up in two bags. Upon the door being opened, Mademoiselle L. appeared and took from his hands one of the bags, while the old lady relieved him of the other. He then bowed and departed. Did not see any person in the street at the time. It is a bye-street — very lonely.

William Bird, tailor, deposes that he was one of the party who entered the house. Is an Englishman. Has lived in Paris two years. Was one of the first to ascend the stairs. Heard the voices in contention. The gruff voice was that of a Frenchman. Could make out several words, but cannot now remember all. Heard distinctly '*sacre*' and '*mon Dieu.*' There was a sound at the moment as if of several persons struggling — a scraping and scuffling sound. The shrill voice was very loud — louder than the gruff one. Is sure that it was not the voice of an Englishman. Appeared to be that of a German. Might have been a woman's voice. Does not understand German.

"Four of the above-named witnesses being recalled, deposed that the door of the chamber in which was found the body of Mademoiselle L. was locked on the inside when the party reached it. Every thing was perfectly silent — no groans or noises of any kind. Upon forcing the door no person was seen. The windows, both of the back and front room, were down and firmly fastened from within. A door between the two rooms was closed but not locked. The door leading from the front room into the passage was locked, with the key on the inside. A small room in the front of the house, on the fourth story, at the head of the passage, was open, the door being ajar. This room was crowded with old beds, boxes, and so forth. These were carefully removed and searched. There was not an inch of any portion of the house which was not carefully searched. Sweeps were sent up and down the chimneys. The house was a four story one, with garrets (*mansardes*).[1] A trap-door on the roof was nailed down very securely — did not appear to have been opened for years. The time elapsing between the hearing of the voices in contention and the breaking open of the room door, was variously stated by the witnesses. Some made it as short as three minutes — some as long as five. The door was opened with difficulty.[2]

"*Alfonzo Garcio*, undertaker, deposes that he resides in

1 *mansardes* - kind of loft

2 Now, back to *Law and Order.*

the Rue Morgue. Is a native of Spain. Was one of the party who entered the house. Did not proceed up stairs. Is nervous, and was apprehensive of the consequences of agitation. Heard the voices in contention. The gruff voice was that of a Frenchman. Could not distinguish what was said. The shrill voice was that of an Englishman — is sure of this. Does not understand the English language, but judges by the intonation.

"*Alberto Montani*, confectioner, deposes that he was among the first to ascend the stairs. Heard the voices in question. The gruff voice was that of a Frenchman. Distinguished several words. The speaker appeared to be expostulating. Could not make out the words of the shrill voice. Spoke quick and unevenly. Thinks it the voice of a Russian. Corroborates the general testimony. Is an Italian. Never conversed with a native of Russia.

"Several witnesses, recalled, here testified that the chimneys of all the rooms on the fourth story were too narrow to admit the passage of a human being. By 'sweeps' were meant cylindrical sweeping-brushes, such as are employed by those who clean chimneys. These brushes were passed up and down every flue in the house. There is no back passage by which any one could have descended while the party proceeded up stairs. The body of Mademoiselle L'Espanaye was so firmly wedged in the chimney that it could not be got down until four or five of the party united their strength.[1]

"*Paul Dumas*, physician, deposes that he was called to view the bodies about daybreak. They were both then lying on the sacking of the bedstead in the chamber where Mademoiselle L. was found. The corpse of the young lady

1 Please direct all questions on this subject to: "Santa – North Pole."

was much bruised and excoriated. The fact that it had been thrust up the chimney would sufficiently account for these appearances.[1] The throat was greatly chafed. There were several deep scratches just below the chin, together with a series of livid spots which were evidently the impression of fingers. The face was fearfully discolored, and the eyeballs protruded. The tongue had been partially bitten through. A large bruise was discovered upon the pit of the stomach, produced, apparently, by the pressure of a knee. In the opinion of M. Dumas, Mademoiselle L'Espanaye had been throttled to death by some person or persons unknown. The corpse of the mother was horribly mutilated. All the bones of the right leg and arm were more or less shattered. The left *tibia* much splintered, as well as all the ribs of the left side. Whole body dreadfully bruised and discolored. It was not possible to say how the injuries had been inflicted. A heavy club of wood, or a broad bar of iron — a chair — any large, heavy, and obtuse[2] weapon have produced such results, if wielded by the hands of a very powerful man. No woman could have inflicted the blows with any weapon. The head of the deceased, when seen by witness, was entirely separated from the body, and was also greatly shattered. The throat had evidently been cut with some very sharp instrument — probably with a razor.[3]

"*Alexandre Etienne*, surgeon, was called with M. Dumas to view the bodies. Corroborated the testimony and the opinions of M. Dumas.

"Nothing further of importance was elicited, although several other persons were examined. A murder so mysterious, and so perplexing in all its particulars, was

1 No kidding.

2 obtuse - blunt

3 So, ol' Edgar nailed the *CSI* approach over 150 years ago.

never before committed in Paris — if indeed a murder has been committed at all. The police are entirely at fault — an unusual occurrence in affairs of this nature. There is not, however, the shadow of a clew apparent."

The evening edition of the paper stated that the greatest excitement continued in the Quartier St. Roch — that the premises in question had been carefully re-searched, and fresh examinations of witnesses instituted, but all to no purpose. A postscript,[1] however, mentioned that Adolphe Le Bon[2] had been arrested and imprisoned — although nothing appeared to criminate[3] him beyond the facts already detailed.

Dupin seemed singularly interested in the progress of this affair — at least so I judged from his manner, for he made no comments. It was only after the announcement that Le Bon had been imprisoned, that he asked me my opinion respecting the murders.

I could merely agree with all Paris in considering them an insoluble mystery. I saw no means by which it would be possible to trace the murderer.

[4]"We must not judge of the means," said Dupin, "by this shell of an examination. The Parisian police, so much extolled for *acumen*, are cunning, but no more. There is no method in their proceedings, beyond the method of the moment. They make a vast parade of measures; but, not unfrequently, these are so ill-adapted to the objects proposed, as to put us in mind of Monsieur Jourdain's calling for his *robe-de-chambre* — *pour mieux entendre la musique*.[5] The results attained by them are not unfrequently surprising, but, for the most part, are brought about by simple diligence and activity. When these qualities are unavailing, their schemes fail. Vidocq,[6]

1 postscript - additional info

2 The messenger from the bank.

3 criminate - incriminate

4 Here's where the chess vs. checkers approach comes in.

5 Calling for his dressing gown in order to hear the music better. As in: it made no sense.

6 A former, real, investigator for the Paris police.

for example, was a good guesser, and a persevering man. But, without educated thought, he erred continually by the very intensity of his investigations. He impaired his vision by holding the object too close. He might see, perhaps, one or two points with unusual clearness, but in so doing he, necessarily, lost sight of the matter as a whole. Thus there is such a thing as being too profound. Truth is not always in a well.[1] In fact, as regards the more important knowledge, I do believe that she[2] is invariably superficial. The depth lies in the valleys where we seek her, and not upon the mountain-tops where she is found. The modes and sources of this kind of error are well typified in the contemplation of the heavenly bodies. To look at a star by glances — to view it in a side-long way, by turning toward it the exterior portions of the *retina* (more susceptible of feeble impressions of light than the interior), is to behold the star distinctly — is to have the best appreciation of its lustre — a lustre which grows dim just in proportion as we turn our vision *fully* upon it. A greater number of rays actually fall upon the eye in the latter case, but in the former, there is the more refined capacity for comprehension. By undue profundity we perplex and enfeeble thought;[3] and it is possible to make even Venus herself vanish from the firmament by a scrutiny too sustained, too concentrated, or too direct.

"As for these murders, let us enter into some examinations for ourselves, before we make up an opinion respecting them. An inquiry will afford us amusement," [I thought this an odd term, so applied, but said nothing] "and besides, Le Bon once rendered me a service for which I am not ungrateful. We will go and see the premises with

1 down deep

2 she - truth

3 Too many facts, like too bright a light, can hide the truth.

our own eyes. I know G —, the Prefect of Police, and shall have no difficulty in obtaining the necessary permission."

The permission was obtained, and we proceeded at once to the Rue Morgue. This is one of those miserable thoroughfares which intervene between the Rue Richelieu and the Rue St. Roch.[1] It was late in the afternoon when we reached it, as this quarter is at a great distance from that in which we resided. The house was readily found; for there were still many persons gazing up at the closed shutters, with an objectless curiosity, from the opposite side of the way.[2] It was an ordinary Parisian house, with a gateway, on one side of which was a glazed watch-box, with a sliding panel in the window, indicating a *loge de concierge*. Before going in we walked up the street, turned down an alley, and then, again turning, passed in the rear of the building — Dupin, meanwhile, examining the whole neighborhood, as well as the house, with a minuteness[3] of attention for which I could see no possible object.

Retracing our steps we came again to the front of the dwelling, rang, and having shown our credentials, were admitted by the agents in charge. We went up stairs — into the chamber where the body of Mademoiselle L'Espanaye had been found, and where both the deceased still lay. The disorders of the room had, as usual, been suffered to exist. I saw nothing beyond what had been stated in the *Gazette des Tribunaux*.[4] Dupin scrutinized every thing — not excepting the bodies of the victims. We then went into the other rooms, and into the yard; a *gendarme* accompanying us throughout. The examination occupied us until dark, when we took our departure. On our way home my companion stepped in for a moment at the office of one of

1 Right behind the DQ (just kidding).

2 The kind of characters who are charter members of the "Get a Life" club.

3 minuteness - closeness

4 newspaper

the daily papers.

I have said that the whims of my friend were manifold, and that *Je les ménagais*: — for this phrase there is no English equivalent.[1] It was his humor,[2] now, to decline all conversation on the subject of the murder, until about noon the next day. He then asked me, suddenly, if I had observed any thing *peculiar* at the scene of the atrocity.

1 Then thanks so much for using it, Eddy.

2 humor - mood

There was something in his manner of emphasizing the word "peculiar," which caused me to shudder, without knowing why.[3]

3 Which is peculiar that "peculiar" would upset him in a pecul…Oh never mind.

"No, nothing *peculiar*," I said; "nothing more, at least, than we both saw stated in the paper."

"*The Gazette,*'" he replied, "has not entered, I fear, into the unusual horror of the thing. But dismiss the idle opinions of this print. It appears to me that this mystery is considered insoluble, for the very reason which should cause it to be regarded as easy of solution — I mean for the *outré*[4] character of its features. The police are confounded

4 *outré* - strange

by the seeming absence of motive — not for the murder itself — but for the atrocity of the murder. They are puzzled, too, by the seeming impossibility of reconciling the voices heard in contention, with the facts that no one was discovered upstairs but the assassinated Mademoiselle L'Espanaye, and that there were no means of egress without the notice of the party ascending. The wild disorder of the room; the corpse thrust, with the head downward, up the chimney; the frightful mutilation of the body of the old lady; these considerations, with those just mentioned, and others which I need not mention, have sufficed to paralyze the powers, by putting completely at fault the boasted *acumen*,[1] of the government agents. They have fallen into the gross but common error of confounding the unusual with the abstruse.[2] But it is by these deviations[3] from the plane of the ordinary, that reason feels its way, if at all, in its search for the true. In investigations such as we are now pursuing, it should not be so much asked 'what has occurred,' as 'what has occurred that has never occurred before.' In fact, the facility with which I shall arrive, or have arrived, at the solution of this mystery, is in the direct ratio of its apparent insolubility[4] in the eyes of the police."

I stared at the speaker in mute astonishment.

"I am now awaiting," continued he, looking toward the door of our apartment — "I am now awaiting a person who, although perhaps not the perpetrator[5] of these butcheries, must have been in some measure implicated in their perpetration. Of the worst portion of the crimes committed, it is probable that he is innocent. I hope that I am right in this supposition; for upon it I build my expectation of reading the entire riddle. I look for the man here — in this room — every moment. It is true that he may not arrive; but the probability is that he will. Should he come, it will be necessary to detain him. Here are pistols; and we both know how to use them when occasion demands their use."[6]

I took the pistols, scarcely knowing what I did, or believing what I heard, while Dupin went on, very much as if in a soliloquy. I have already spoken of his abstract manner at such times. His discourse was addressed to myself; but his voice, although by no means loud, had that intonation which is commonly employed in speaking to

1 boasted *acumen* - expert abilities

2 abstruse - complex, hard to understand

3 deviations - departure

4 insolubility - unsolvability

5 perpetrator - person who committed

6 Very unusual for Poe to "give" a character a gun, but this was a whole new genre (style of writing).

some one at a great distance. His eyes, vacant in expression, regarded only the wall.

"That the voices heard in contention," he said, "by the party upon the stairs, were not the voices of the women themselves, was fully proved by the evidence. This relieves us of all doubt upon the question whether the old lady could have first destroyed the daughter, and afterward have committed suicide. I speak of this point chiefly for the sake of method; for the strength of Madame L'Espanaye would have been utterly unequal to the task of thrusting her daughter's corpse up the chimney as it was found; and the nature of the wounds upon her own person entirely precludes the idea of self-destruction. Murder, then, has been committed by some third party; and the voices of this third party were those heard in contention.[1] Let me now advert[2] — not to the whole testimony respecting these voices — but to what was *peculiar* in that testimony. Did you observe any thing peculiar about it?"

I remarked that, while all the witnesses agreed in supposing the gruff voice to be that of a Frenchman, there was much disagreement in regard to the shrill, or, as one individual termed it, the harsh voice.

"That was the evidence itself," said Dupin, "but it was not the peculiarity of the evidence. You have observed nothing distinctive. Yet there *was* something to be observed. The witnesses, as you remark, agreed about the gruff voice; they were here unanimous. But in regard to the shrill voice, the peculiarity is — not that they disagreed — but that, while an Italian, an Englishman, a Spaniard, a Hollander, and a Frenchman attempted to describe it, each one spoke of it as that *of a foreigner*. Each is sure that it

1 contention - arguing

2 advert - focus on

was not the voice of one of his own countrymen. Each likens it — not to the voice of an individual of any nation with whose language he is conversant — but the converse. The Frenchman supposes it the voice of a Spaniard, and 'might have distinguished some words *had he been acquainted with the Spanish.*' The Dutchman maintains it to have been that of a Frenchman; but we find it stated that '*not understanding French this witness was examined through an interpreter.*' The Englishman thinks it the voice of a German, and 'does *not understand German.*' The Spaniard 'is sure' that it was that of an Englishman, but 'judges by the intonation' altogether, '*as he has no knowledge of the English.*' The Italian believes it the voice of a Russian, but '*has never conversed with a native of Russia.*' A second Frenchman differs, moreover, with the first, and is positive that the voice was that of an Italian; but, *not being cognizant of that tongue*, is, like the Spaniard, 'convinced by the intonation.' Now, how strangely unusual must that voice have really been, about which such testimony as this *could* have been elicited! — in whose *tones*, even, denizens of the five great divisions of Europe could recognize nothing familiar![1] You will say that it might have been the voice of an Asiatic — of an African. Neither Asiatics nor Africans abound in Paris; but, without denying the inference, I will now merely call your attention to three points. The voice is termed by one witness 'harsh rather than shrill.' It is represented by two others to have been 'quick and *unequal.*' No words — no sounds resembling words — were by any witness mentioned as distinguishable.

"I know not," continued Dupin, "what impression I

[1] Doesn't that happen every day at the UN?

may have made, so far, upon your own understanding; but I do not hesitate to say that legitimate deductions even from this portion of the testimony — the portion respecting the gruff and shrill voices — are in themselves sufficient to engender[1] a suspicion which should give direction to all farther progress in the investigation of the mystery. I said 'legitimate deductions;' but my meaning is not thus fully expressed. I designed to imply that the deductions are the *sole* proper ones, and that the suspicion arises *inevitably* from them as the single result. What the suspicion is, however, I will not say just yet. I merely wish you to bear in mind that, with myself, it was sufficiently forcible to give a definite form — a certain tendency — to my inquiries in the chamber.

"Let us now transport ourselves, in fancy,[2] to this chamber. What shall we first seek here? The means of egress[3] employed by the murderers. It is not too much to say that neither of us believe in preternatural[4] events. Madame and Mademoiselle L'Espanaye were not destroyed by spirits. The doers of the deed were material,[5] and escaped materially. Then how? Fortunately there is but one mode of reasoning upon the point, and that mode *must* lead us to a definite decision. Let us examine, each by each, the possible means of egress. It is clear that the assassins were in the room where Mademoiselle L'Espanaye was found, or at least in the room adjoining, when the party ascended the stairs. It is, then, only from these two apartments that we have to seek issues. The police have laid bare the floors, the ceiling, and the masonry of the walls, in every direction. No *secret* issues could have escaped their vigilance. But, not trusting to *their* eyes,

1 engender - create

2 Pretending - the 1800's version of virtual reality.

3 Not a bird – it's an exit.

4 preternatural - supernatural

5 Madonna did it?

I examined with my own. There were, then, *no* secret issues. Both doors leading from the rooms into the passage were securely locked, with the keys inside. Let us turn to the chimneys. These, although of ordinary width for some eight or ten feet above the hearths, will not admit, throughout their extent, the body of a large cat. The impossibility of egress, by means already stated, being thus absolute, we are reduced to the windows. Through those of the front room no one could have escaped without notice from the crowd in the street. The murderers *must* have passed, then, through those of the back room. Now, brought to this conclusion in so unequivocal[1] a manner as we are, it is not our part, as reasoners, to reject it on account of apparent impossibilities. It is only left for us to prove that these apparent 'impossibilities' are, in reality, not such.

"There are two windows in the chamber. One of them is unobstructed by furniture, and is wholly visible. The lower portion of the other is hidden from view by the head of the unwieldy bedstead which is thrust close up against it. The former was found securely fastened from within. It resisted the utmost force of those who endeavored to raise it. A large gimlet-hole[2] had been pierced in its frame to the left, and a very stout nail was found fitted therein, nearly to the head. Upon examining the other window, a similar nail was seen similarly fitted in it; and a vigorous attempt to raise this sash failed also. The police were now entirely satisfied that egress had not been in these directions. And, *therefore*, it was thought a matter of supererogation[3] to withdraw the nails and open the windows.

"My own examination was somewhat more particular,

1 unequivocal - certain

2 gimlet-hole - hole made by a sharp pointed tool

3 supererogation - unnecessary

and was so for the reason I have just given — because here it was, I knew, that all apparent impossibilities *must* be proved to be not such in reality.

"I proceeded to think thus — *a posteriori*.[1] The murderers *did* escape from one of these windows. This being so, they could not have re-fastened the sashes from the inside, as they were found fastened — the consideration which put a stop, through its obviousness, to the scrutiny[2] of the police in this quarter. Yet the sashes *were* fastened. They *must*, then, have the power of fastening themselves. There was no escape from this conclusion. I stepped to the unobstructed casement, withdrew the nail with some difficulty, and attempted to raise the sash. It resisted all my efforts, as I had anticipated. A concealed spring must, I now knew, exist; and this corroboration of my idea convinced me that my premises, at least, were correct, however mysterious still appeared the circumstances attending the nails. A careful search soon brought to light the hidden spring. I pressed it, and, satisfied with the discovery, forebore[3] to upraise the sash.

"I now replaced the nail and regarded it attentively. A person passing out through this window might have reclosed it, and the spring would have caught — but the nail could not have been replaced. The conclusion was plain, and again narrowed in the field of my investigations. The assassins *must* have escaped through the other window. Supposing, then, the springs upon each sash to be the same, as was probable, there *must* be found a difference between the nails, or at least between the modes of their fixture. Getting upon the sacking of the bedstead, I looked

1 Facts obtained by observation or experiment.

2 scrutiny - inspection

3 forebore - attempted

over the head-board minutely at the second casement. Passing my hand down behind the board, I readily discovered and pressed the spring, which was, as I had supposed, identical in character with its neighbor. I now looked at the nail. It was as stout as the other, and apparently fitted in the same manner — driven in nearly up to the head.

"You will say that I was puzzled; but, if you think so, you must have misunderstood the nature of the inductions.[1] To use a sporting phrase, I had not been once 'at fault.' The scent had never for an instant been lost. There was no flaw in any link of the chain. I had traced the secret to its ultimate result, — and that result was *the nail*. It had, I say, in every respect, the appearance of its fellow in the other window; but this fact was an absolute nullity[2] (conclusive as it might seem to be) when compared with the consideration that here, at this point, terminated the clew.[3] 'There *must* be something wrong,' I said, 'about the nail.' I touched it; and the head, with about a quarter of an inch of the shank came off in my fingers. The rest of the shank was in the gimlet-hole, where it had been broken off. The fracture was an old one (for its edges were incrusted with rust), and had apparently been accomplished by the blow of a hammer, which had partially imbedded, in the top of the bottom sash, the head portion of the nail. I now carefully replaced this head portion in the indentation whence I had taken it, and the resemblance to a perfect nail was complete — the fissure was invisible. Pressing the spring, I gently raised the sash for a few inches; the head went up with it, remaining firm in its bed. I closed the window, and the semblance of the whole nail was again perfect.[4]

1 Conclusions drawn from the observation.

2 Its appearance didn't matter.

3 Don't you wish he'd spell "clue" correctly?

4 Pretty spiffy call, Dupin. Although some critics of Poe call the whole nail secret spring set-up totally bogus. But give Eddy a break; nobody'd done this before. Jeez!

"The riddle, so far, was now unriddled.[1] The assassin had escaped through the window which looked upon the bed. Dropping of its own accord upon his exit (or perhaps purposely closed), it had become fastened by the spring; and it was the retention of this spring which had been mistaken by the police for that of the nail, — farther inquiry being thus considered unnecessary.

"The next question is that of the mode of descent. Upon this point I had been satisfied in my walk with you around the building. About five feet and a half from the casement in question there runs a lightning-rod. From this rod it would have been impossible for any one to reach the window itself, to say nothing of entering it. I observed, however, that shutters of the fourth story were of the peculiar kind called by Parisian carpenters *ferrades* — a kind rarely employed at the present day, but frequently seen upon very old mansions at Lyons and Bourdeaux. They are in the form of an ordinary door (a single, not a folding door), except that the upper half is latticed or worked in open trellis — thus affording an excellent hold for the hands. In the present instance these shutters are fully three feet and a half broad. When we saw them from the rear of the house, they were both about half open — that is to say, they stood off at right angles from the wall. It is probable that the police, as well as myself, examined the back of the tenement; but, if so, in looking at these *ferrades* in the line of their breadth (as they must have done), they did not perceive this great breadth itself,[2] or, at all events, failed to take it into due consideration.[3] In fact, having once satisfied themselves that no egress could have been made in this quarter, they would naturally bestow here a

1 "Unriddled"? Okay, now he's making up words.

2 How wide they really were.

3 They didn't look that wide when seen head-on as they were in the back of the house.

very cursory[1] examination. It was clear to me, however, that the shutter belonging to the window at the head of the bed, would, if swung fully back to the wall, reach to within two feet of the lightning-rod. It was also evident that, by exertion of a very unusual degree of activity and courage, an entrance into the window, from the rod, might have been thus effected. By reaching to the distance of two feet and a half (we now suppose the shutter open to its whole extent) a robber might have taken a firm grasp upon the trellis-work. Letting go, then, his hold upon the rod, placing his feet securely against the wall, and springing boldly from it, he might have swung the shutter so as to close it, and, if we imagine the window open at the time, might even have swung himself into the room.

"I wish you to bear especially in mind that I have spoken of a *very* unusual degree of activity as requisite to success in so hazardous and so difficult a feat. It is my design to show you first, that the thing might possibly have been accomplished: — but, secondly and *chiefly*, I wish to impress upon your understanding the *very extraordinary* — the almost preternatural[2] character of that agility which could have accomplished it.

"You will say, no doubt, using the language of the law, that 'to make out my case,' I should rather undervalue, than insist upon a full estimation of the activity required in this matter. This may be the practice in law, but it is not the usage of reason. My ultimate object is only the truth. My immediate purpose is to lead you to place in juxtaposition,[3] that *very unusual* activity of which I have just spoken, with that *very peculiar* shrill (or harsh) and *unequal* voice, about whose nationality no two persons could be found to

1 cursory - superficial

2 Again with the abnormal weird stuff.

3 juxtaposition - compare side by side

agree, and in whose utterance no syllabification[1] could be detected."

At these words a vague and half-formed conception of the meaning of Dupin flitted over my mind. I seemed to be upon the verge of comprehension, without power to comprehend — as men, at times, find themselves upon the brink of remembrance, without being able, in the end, to remember.[2] My friend went on with his discourse.

"You will see," he said, "that I have shifted the question from the mode of egress to that of ingress.[3] It was my design to suggest the idea that both were effected in the same manner, at the same point. Let us now revert to the interior of the room. Let us survey the appearances here. The drawers of the bureau, it is said, had been rifled, although many articles of apparel still remained within them. The conclusion here is absurd. It is a mere guess — a very silly one — and no more. How are we to know that the articles found in the drawers were not all these drawers had originally contained? Madame L'Espanaye and her daughter lived an exceedingly retired life — saw no company — seldom went out — had little use for numerous changes of habiliment.[4] Those found were at least of as good quality as any likely to be possessed by these ladies. If a thief had taken any, why did he not take the best — why did he not take all? In a word, why did he abandon four thousand francs in gold to encumber himself with a bundle of linen? The gold *was* abandoned. Nearly the whole sum mentioned by Monsieur Mignaud, the banker, was discovered, in bags, upon the floor. I wish you therefore, to discard from your thoughts the blundering idea of *motive*, engendered in the brains of the police by

1 He just had to be making "syllabification" up — but it means, kind of, that the voice that was heard was just sounds and no real syllables.

2 There was a country song with a title like this: "I Remembered a Song About Someone I Can't Remember," sung by Barry "The Fish" Melton, Flying Fish Records, 1978. Really. I swear.

3 Also not a bird, but how the killer entered.

4 habiliment - clothes

that portion of the evidence which speaks of money delivered at the door of the house. Coincidences ten times as remarkable as this (the delivery of the money, and murder committed within three days upon the party receiving it), happen to all of us every hour of our lives, without attracting even momentary notice. Coincidences, in general, are great stumbling-blocks in the way of that class of thinkers who have been educated to know nothing of the theory of probabilities — that theory to which the most glorious objects of human research are indebted for the most glorious of illustration.[1] In the present instance, had the gold been gone, the fact of its delivery three days before would have formed something more than a coincidence. It would have been corroborative of this idea of motive. But, under the real circumstances of the case, if we are to suppose gold the motive of this outrage, we must also imagine the perpetrator so vacillating[2] an idiot as to have abandoned his gold and his motive together.

"Keeping now steadily in mind the points to which I have drawn your attention — that peculiar voice, that unusual agility, and that startling absence of motive in a murder so singularly atrocious as this — let us glance at the butchery itself.[3] Here is a woman strangled to death by manual strength, and thrust up a chimney head downward. Ordinary assassins employ no such mode of murder as this. Least of all, do they thus dispose of the murdered. In the manner of thrusting the corpse up the chimney, you will admit that there was something *excessively outré*[4] — something altogether irreconcilable with our common notions of human action, even when we suppose the actors the most depraved of men. Think, too, how great

1 I don't know about you, but it's feeling like Dupin is copping a really arrogant 'tude.

2 Let's go with "unstable."

3 You look, I'll wait in the car.

4 Off the radar.

must have been that strength which could have thrust the body *up* such an aperture so forcibly that the united vigor of several persons was found barely sufficient to drag it *down*!

"Turn, now, to other indications of the employment of a vigor most marvellous.[1] On the hearth were thick tresses — very thick tresses — of gray human hair. These had been torn out by the roots.[2] You are aware of the great force necessary in tearing thus from the head even twenty or thirty hairs together. You saw the locks in question as well as myself. Their roots (a hideous sight!) were clotted with fragments of the flesh of the scalp — sure token of the prodigious power which had been exerted in uprooting perhaps half a million of hairs at a time. The throat of the old lady was not merely cut, but the head absolutely severed from the body: the instrument was a mere razor. I wish you also to look at the *brutal* ferocity of these deeds.[3] Of the bruises upon the body of Madame L'Espanaye I do not speak. Monsieur Dumas, and his worthy co-adjutor Monsieur Etienne, have pronounced that they were inflicted by some obtuse instrument; and so far these gentlemen are very correct. The obtuse instrument was clearly the stone pavement in the yard, upon which the victim had fallen from the window which looked in upon the bed. This idea, however simple it may now seem, escaped the police for the same reason that the breadth of the shutters escaped them — because, by the affair of the nails, their perceptions had been hermetically[4] sealed against the possibility of the windows having ever been opened at all.

"If now, in addition to all these things, you have

1 He doesn't mean he's thrilled by the killer's strength, just that it's amazingly powerful.

2 And I'm not just a client of The Hair Club For Men – I'm the…YEE-OWWW!

3 Uh, we're not going out for sushi after this, are we?

4 hermetically - airtight

properly reflected upon the odd disorder of the chamber, we have gone so far as to combine the ideas of an agility astounding, a strength superhuman, a ferocity brutal, a butchery without motive, a *grotesquerie* in horror absolutely alien from humanity, and a voice foreign in tone to the ears of men of many nations, and devoid of all distinct or intelligible syllabification. What result, then, has ensued? What impression have I made upon your fancy?"[1]

I felt a creeping of the flesh as Dupin asked me the question. "A madman," I said, "has done this deed — some raving maniac, escaping from a neighboring *Maison de Santé*."[2]

"In some respects," he replied, "your idea is not irrelevant. But the voices of madmen, even in their wildest paroxysms,[3] are never found to tally with that peculiar voice heard upon the stairs. Madmen are of some nation, and their language, however incoherent in its words, has always the coherence of syllabification. Besides, the hair of a madman is not such as I now hold in my hand. I disentangled this little tuft from the rigidly clutched fingers of Madame L'Espanaye.[4] Tell me what you can make of it."

"Dupin!" I said, completely unnerved; "this hair is most unusual — this is no *human* hair."[5]

"I have not asserted that it is," said he; "but, before we decide this point, I wish you to glance at the little sketch I have here traced upon this paper. It is a *fac-simile* drawing of what has been described in one portion of the testimony as 'dark bruises and deep indentations of finger nails' upon the throat of Mademoiselle L'Espanaye, and in

1 O.J. did it.

2 *Maison de Santé* - Insane Asylum

3 paroxysms - seizure

4 Plot hole warning: The cops may have been stupid, but they didn't see the hair in her hand? Aw, come on.

5 Plot leap of logic warning: He knows this…how?

another (by Messrs. Dumas and Etienne) as a 'series of livid spots, evidently the impressions of fingers.'

"You will perceive," continued my friend, spreading out the paper upon the table before us, "that this drawing gives the idea of a firm and fixed hold. There is no *slipping* apparent. Each finger has retained — possibly until the death of the victim — the fearful grasp by which it originally imbedded itself. Attempt, now, to place all your fingers, at the same time, in the respective impressions as you see them."

I made the attempt in vain.

"We are possibly not giving this matter a fair trial," he said. "The paper is spread out upon a plane surface; but the human throat is cylindrical. Here is a billet of wood, the circumference of which is about that of the throat. Wrap the drawing around it, and try the experiment again."

I did so; but the difficulty was even more obvious than before. "This," I said, "is the mark of no human hand."

"Read now," replied Dupin, "this passage from Cuvier."

It was a minute anatomical and generally descriptive account of the large fulvous[1] Ourang-Outang of the East Indian islands. The gigantic stature, the prodigious strength and activity, the wild ferocity, and the imitative propensities of these mammalia[2] are sufficiently well known to all. I understood the full horrors of the murder at once.

"The description of the digits,"[3] said I, as I made an end of reading, "is in exact accordance with this drawing. I see that no animal but an Ourang-Outang, of the species

1 fulvous - tawny

2 mammalia - mammals

3 digits - fingers

here mentioned, could have impressed the indentations as you have traced them. This tuft of tawny hair, too, is identical in character with that of the beast of Cuvier. But I cannot possibly comprehend the particulars of this frightful mystery. Besides, there were *two* voices heard in contention, and one of them was unquestionably the voice of a Frenchman."

"True; and you will remember an expression attributed almost unanimously, by the evidence, to this voice, — the expression, '*mon Dieu*' This, under the circumstances, has been justly characterized by one of the witnesses (Montani, the confectioner) as an expression of remonstrance[1] or expostulation.[2] Upon these two words, therefore, I have mainly built my hopes of a full solution of the riddle. A Frenchman was cognizant of the murder. It is possible — indeed it is far more than probable — that he was innocent of all participation in the bloody transactions which took place. The Ourang-Outang may have escaped from him. He may have traced it to the chamber; but, under the agitating circumstances which ensued, he could never have re-captured it. It is still at large. I will not pursue these guesses — for I have no right to call them more — since the shades of reflection upon which they are based are scarcely of sufficient depth to be appreciable by my own intellect, and since I could not pretend to make them intelligible to the understanding of another.[3] We will call them guesses, then, and speak of them as such.[4] If the Frenchman in question is indeed, as I suppose, innocent of this atrocity, this advertisement, which I left last night upon our return home, at the office of '*Le Monde*,' (a paper devoted to the shipping interest, and much sought by sailors), will bring him to our residence."

1 remonstrance - protest

2 expostulation - disapproval

3 Dupin's still feeling he's guessing to a degree.

4 See? I was right. No, actually I read ahead.

He handed me a paper, and I read thus:

CAUGHT — In the Bois de Boulogne, early in the morning of the — inst. (the morning of the murder), a very large, tawny Ourang-Outang of the Bornese species. The owner (who is ascertained to be a sailor, belonging to a Maltese vessel) may have the animal again, upon identifying it satisfactorily, and paying a few charges arising from its capture and keeping. Call at No. — , Rue — Faubourg St. Germain — *au troisiéme*."

"How was it possible," I asked, "that you should know the man to be a sailor, and belonging to a Maltese vessel?"

"I do *not know* it," said Dupin. "I am not *sure* of it. Here, however, is a small piece of ribbon, which from its form, and from its greasy appearance, has evidently been used in tying the hair in one of those long *queues*[1] of which sailors are so fond. Moreover, this knot is one which few besides sailors can tie, and is peculiar to the Maltese. I picked the ribbon up at the foot of the lightning-rod.[2] It could not have belonged to either of the deceased.[3] Now if, after all, I am wrong in my induction from this ribbon, that the Frenchman was a sailor belonging to a Maltese vessel, still I can have done no harm in saying what I did in the advertisement. If I am right, a great point is gained. Cognizant[4] although innocent of the murder, the Frenchman will naturally hesitate about replying to the advertisement — about demanding the Ourang-Outang. He will reason thus: — 'I am innocent; I am poor; my Ourang-Outang is of great value — to one in my circumstances a fortune of itself — why should I lose it through idle apprehensions of danger? Here it is, within my grasp. It was found in the Bois de Boulogne —

1 *queues* - ponytail

2 We're talking more clues that are waaay too convenient, here.

3 Yeah? Why couldn't the daughter have had a secret Maltese sailor boyfriend, huh?

4 Cognizant - aware

at a vast distance from the scene of that butchery. How can it ever be suspected that a brute beast should have done the deed? The police are at fault — they have failed to procure the slightest clew. Should they even trace the animal, it would be impossible to prove me cognizant of the murder, or to implicate me in guilt on account of that cognizance. Above all, *I am known*. The advertiser designates me as the possessor of the beast. I am not sure to what limit his knowledge may extend. Should I avoid claiming a property of so great value, which it is known that I possess, I will render the animal at least, liable to suspicion. It is not my policy to attract attention either to myself or to the beast. I will answer the advertisement, get the Ourang-Outang, and keep it close until this matter has blown over.'"

At this moment we heard a step upon the stairs.

"Be ready," said Dupin, "with your pistols, but neither use them nor show them until at a signal from myself."[1]

The front door of the house had been left open, and the visitor had entered, without ringing, and advanced several steps upon the staircase. Now, however, he seemed to hesitate. Presently we heard him descending. Dupin was moving quickly to the door, when we again heard him coming up. He did not turn back a second time, but stepped up with decision, and rapped at the door of our chamber.

"Come in," said Dupin, in a cheerful and hearty tone.

A man entered. He was a sailor, evidently, — a tall, stout, and muscular-looking person, with a certain daredevil expression of countenance,[2] not altogether unprepossessing.[3] His face, greatly sunburnt, was more than half hidden by whisker and *mustachio*. He had with

1 "Myself"? Can't he just say "me"?

2 countenance - composure

3 unprepossessing - unappealing

him a huge oaken cudgel,[1] but appeared to be otherwise unarmed.[2] He bowed awkwardly, and bade us "good evening," in French accents, which, although somewhat Neufchatelish,[3] were still sufficiently indicative of a Parisian origin.

"Sit down, my friend," said Dupin. "I suppose you have called about the Ourang-Outang. Upon my word, I almost envy you the possession of him; a remarkably fine, and no doubt a very valuable animal. How old do you suppose him to be?"

The sailor drew a long breath, with the air of a man relieved of some intolerable burden, and then replied, in an assured tone:

"I have no way of telling — but he can't be more than four or five years old. Have you got him here?"

"Oh no; we had no conveniences for keeping him here. He is at a livery stable in the Rue Dubourg, just by. You can get him in the morning. Of course you are prepared to identify the property?"

"To be sure I am, sir."

"I shall be sorry to part with him," said Dupin.

"I don't mean that you should be at all this trouble for nothing, sir," said the man. "Couldn't expect it. Am very willing to pay a reward for the finding of the animal — that is to say, anything in reason."

"Well," replied my friend, "that is all very fair, to be sure. Let me think! — what should I have? Oh! I will tell you. My reward shall be this. You shall give me all the information in your power about these murders in the Rue Morgue."[4]

Dupin said the last words in a very low tone, and very

1 cudgel - club

2 Otherwise?

3 Neufchatel is a creamy cheese, so he's implying the guy...?

4 Oh, slipped it right in!

quietly. Just as quietly, too, he walked toward the door, locked it, and put the key in his pocket. He then drew a pistol from his bosom and placed it, without the least flurry, upon the table.

The sailor's face flushed up as if he were struggling with suffocation. He started to his feet and grasped his cudgel; but the next moment he fell back into his seat, trembling violently, and with the countenance of death itself. He spoke not a word. I pitied him from the bottom of my heart.

"My friend," said Dupin, in a kind tone, "you are alarming yourself unnecessarily — you are indeed. We mean you no harm whatever. I pledge you the honor of a gentleman, and of a Frenchman, that we intend you no injury. I perfectly well know that you are innocent of the atrocities in the Rue Morgue. It will not do, however, to deny that you are in some measure implicated in them. From what I have already said, you must know that I have had means of information about this matter — means of which you could never have dreamed. Now the thing stands thus. You have done nothing which you could have avoided — nothing, certainly, which renders you culpable. You are not even guilty of robbery, when you might have robbed with impunity. You have nothing to conceal. You have no reason for concealment. On the other hand, you are bound by every principle of honor to confess all you know. An innocent man is now imprisoned, charged with that crime of which you can point out the perpetrator."

The sailor had recovered his presence of mind, in a great measure, while Dupin uttered these words; but his original boldness of bearing was all gone.

"So help me God!" said he, after a brief pause, "I *will* tell you all I know about this affair; — but I do not expect you to believe one half I say — I would be a fool indeed if I did. Still, I *am* innocent, and I will make a clean breast if I die for it."

What he stated was, in substance, this. He had lately made a voyage to the Indian Archipelago.[1] A party, of which he formed one, landed at Borneo, and passed into the interior on an excursion of pleasure. Himself and a companion had captured the Ourang-Outang. This companion dying, the animal fell into his own exclusive possession. After great trouble, occasioned by the intractable[2] ferocity of his captive during the home voyage, he at length succeeded in lodging it safely at his own residence in Paris,[3] where, not to attract toward himself the unpleasant curiosity of his neighbors, he kept it carefully secluded, until such time as it should recover from a wound in the foot, received from a splinter on board ship. His ultimate design was to sell it.

Returning home from some sailor's frolic on the night, or rather in the morning, of the murder, he found the beast occupying his own bedroom,[4] into which it had broken from a closet adjoining, where it had been, as was thought, securely confined. Razor in hand, and fully lathered, it was sitting before a looking-glass, attempting the operation of shaving, in which it had no doubt previously watched its master through the keyhole of the closet. Terrified at the sight of so dangerous a weapon in the possession of an animal so ferocious, and so well able to use it, the man, for some moments, was at a loss what to do. He had been accustomed, however, to quiet the

1 Archipelago - group of islands

2 intractable - wild, cannot be tamed

3 Oh, now there's a smart move.

4 And the #1 thing you don't want to find in your bedroom is....

creature, even in its fiercest moods, by the use of a whip,[1] and to this he now resorted. Upon sight of it, the Ourang-Outang sprang at once through the door of the chamber, down the stairs, and thence, through a window, unfortunately open, into the street.[2]

The Frenchman followed in despair; the ape, razor still in hand, occasionally stopping to look back and gesticulate[3] at his pursuer, until the latter had nearly come up with it. It then again made off. In this manner the chase continued for a long time. The streets were profoundly quiet, as it was nearly three o'clock in the morning. In passing down an alley in the rear of the Rue Morgue, the fugitive's attention was arrested by a light gleaming from the open window of Madame L'Espanaye's chamber, in the fourth story of her house. Rushing to the building, it perceived the lightning-rod, clambered up with inconceivable agility, grasped the shutter, which was thrown fully back against the wall, and, by its means, swung itself directly upon the headboard of the bed. The whole feat did not occupy a minute. The shutter was kicked open again by the Ourang-Outang as it entered the room.

The sailor, in the meantime, was both rejoiced and perplexed. He had strong hopes of now recapturing the brute, as it could scarcely escape from the trap into which it had ventured, except by the rod, where it might be intercepted as it came down. On the other hand, there was much cause for anxiety as to what it might do in the house. This latter reflection urged the man still to follow the fugitive. A lightning-rod is ascended without difficulty, especially by a sailor; but, when he had arrived as high as

[1] Well, that makes perfect sense, no?

[2] Proving that monkeys are smarter than Maltese sailors.

[3] "Gesticulate" means to make hand gestures, but let's not ask which hand gestures the monkey made.

the window, which lay far to his left, his career[1] was stopped; the most that he could accomplish was to reach over so as to obtain a glimpse of the interior of the room. At this glimpse he nearly fell from his hold through excess of horror. Now it was that those hideous shrieks arose upon the night, which had startled from slumber the inmates of the Rue Morgue. Madame L'Espanaye and her daughter, habited[2] in their night clothes, had apparently been occupied in arranging some papers in the iron chest already mentioned, which had been wheeled into the middle of the room. It was open, and its contents lay beside it on the floor. The victims must have been sitting with their backs toward the window; and, from the time elapsing between the ingress of the beast and the screams, it seems probable that it was not immediately perceived. The flapping to of the shutter would naturally have been attributed to the wind.

As the sailor looked in, the gigantic animal had seized Madame L'Espanaye by the hair (which was loose, as she had been combing it), and was flourishing the razor about her face, in imitation of the motions of a barber. The daughter lay prostrate and motionless; she had swooned. The screams and struggles of the old lady (during which the hair was torn from her head) had the effect of changing the probably pacific[3] purposes of the Ourang-Outang into those of wrath.[4] With one determined sweep of its muscular arm it nearly severed her head from her body. The sight of blood inflamed its anger into phrenzy.[5] Gnashing its teeth, and flashing fire from its eyes, it flew upon the body of the girl and embedded its fearful talons in her throat, retaining its grasp until she expired. Its

1 career - rapid course

2 habited - wearing

3 pacific - peaceful
4 wrath - rage

5 phrenzy - frenzy

wandering and wild glances fell at this moment upon the head of the bed, over which the face of its master, rigid with horror, was just discernible.[1] The fury of the beast, who no doubt bore still in mind the dreaded whip, was instantly converted into fear.[2] Conscious of having deserved punishment, it seemed desirous of concealing its bloody deeds, and skipped about the chamber in an agony of nervous agitation; throwing down and breaking the furniture as it moved, and dragging the bed from the bedstead. In conclusion, it seized first the corpse of the daughter, and thrust it up the chimney, as it was found; then that of the old lady, which it immediately hurled through the window headlong.

As the ape approached the casement with its mutilated burden, the sailor shrank aghast to the rod, and, rather gliding than clambering down it, hurried at once home — dreading the consequences of the butchery, and gladly abandoning, in his terror, all solicitude[3] about the fate of the Ourang-Outang. The words heard by the party upon the staircase were the Frenchman's exclamations of horror and affright, commingled[4] with the fiendish jabberings of the brute.

I have scarcely any thing to add. The Ourang-Outang must have escaped from the chamber, by the rod, just before the breaking of the door. It must have closed the window as it passed through it. It was subsequently caught by the owner himself, who obtained for it a very large sum at the *Jardin des Plantes*. Le Bon was instantly released, upon our narration of the circumstances (with some comments from Dupin) at the *bureau* of the Prefect of Police. This functionary,[5] however, well disposed[6] to my

1 discernible - visible

2 Uh oh, monkey blow it big-time.

3 solicitude - concern

4 commingled - mixed

5 functionary - low level worker
6 disposed - friendly

friend, could not altogether conceal his chagrin at the turn which affairs had taken, and was fain[1] to indulge in a sarcasm or two[2] about the propriety[3] of every person minding his own business.

"Let them talk," said Dupin, who had not thought it necessary to reply. "Let him discourse; it will ease his conscience. I am satisfied with having defeated him in his own castle. Nevertheless, that he failed in the solution of this mystery, is by no means that matter for wonder which he supposes it; for, in truth, our friend the prefect is somewhat too cunning to be profound. In his wisdom is no *stamen*. It is all head and no body, like the pictures of the Goddess Laverna — or, at best, all head and shoulders, like a codfish. But he is a good creature after all. I like him especially for one master stroke of cant, by which he has attained his reputation for ingenuity, I mean the way he has '*de nier ce qui est, et d'expliquer ce qui n'est pas.*'"[4] Rousseau, Nouvelle Heloise.

4 A quote from Rousseau which means "to deny that which is and to explain it as that which is not." In other words, it's making up another explanation for reality.

THE MURDERS IN THE RUE MORGUE NOTES

THE MURDERS IN THE RUE MORGUE NOTES

Introduction to The Raven, The Bells, and Annabel Lee

The Raven

Just about everyone has, at least, heard of the poem "The Raven." Even if you haven't, its subject matter does seem kind of obvious (drumroll, please). It's about a raven, right? Uh, not really. Just like everything else Poe wrote, the answer isn't that simple.

Well, it is, but it's not. Sure, a raven shows up in this guy's chamber late at night. And it keeps saying "Nevermore." But we humans have a real funny habit of projecting our feelings and purposes onto animals. And this particular guy gets totally obsessed by what this bird means. It comes out in his questions that he's been mourning the loss of his lover. By the end of the poem he's attaching all kinds of significance to the one word this scrawny crow keeps saying. Ultimately he loses whatever marbles he had left trying to figure out the unknowable. But the bird? It's a bird. Says only one word.

The raven in the poem is considered by many critics to be the catalyst (the excuse), that causes the grieving man to become an emotional wreck. But why does this person put himself through this torture?

Why? Well, we're back to some of the favorite themes Poe liked to dwell on: Death (no surprise there) and Life after death (or at least some world beyond the grave). The fact is that people really do like to torture themselves, and it seems we just can't help it. To support this last theme, pay attention to the way the narrator asks his questions of the bird. He phrases them so that the one answer, "Nevermore," always fits. So, hey, by the fourth time he asks the bird a question, don't you think he has a pretty good idea that it's going to answer "Nevermore"? I mean, hel-lo!

But wait! There's more! We'll also include this handy…oh, sorry. Got carried away. But there is more. And if you read now, there's no shipping and handling.

Poe wrote a very controversial article shortly before his death called "The Philosophy of Composition." In it he outlined, point by point, how he composed "The Raven." He even said it's kind of like a magician showing you the secrets of how he performs his tricks.

One big point he made is that (just like his detective stories) he wrote "The Raven" backwards. No, not the last word first. He said that he first focused on his objective, which was his belief that a poem must have a "unity of effect" – deal with one strong emotion. And that to do this, a poem can be no more than a hundred lines ("The Raven" is 108 – close enough). He also said he decided that the only thing more dramatic than death is the death of a beautiful young woman. And the only thing more painfully romantic is that dead woman mourned by her lover who is left behind in the land of the living. And that this theme of ultimate beauty, the death of the young woman, is the saddest and loveliest of melancholy subjects. All that before ever starting to write.

He described his next step in creating "The Raven," which was coming up with the word "Nevermore" because it had the spookiest "sounds" to the human ear. He then decided the word had to be spoken by something non-human. He chose the raven instead of the parrot because it is a much more ominous and symbolically more powerful image. But we're going to stop right here. Not because – for a lot of you – how he wrote "The Raven" might be a tad bit boring. Heck, that's never before stopped a textbook. No, we're going to stop because many really brilliant writers, critics, and researchers believe that "The Philosophy of Composition" is a crock. Bull. Baloney. They believe Poe wrote the poem first and then made up the whole "Philosophy" many years later to fit the poem.

None other than T.S. Eliot said it was the biggest hoax he ever read. Others believe it's nothing more than shameful self-promotion written in the last days of a life spiraling out of control. There are also those who believe it's completely legit.

In all fairness, the "backwards composition" he swears he used does have many valid points to it. The death of a beautiful young woman is utterly tragic (But even more so is the death of a child. And that he never wrote about). "Nevermore" is a creepy word. His awareness of sounds, of very specific poetic rhythms and structure, are also worthy of consideration.

He does bring up in "Philosophy" that the backwards structure technique is also used by many authors in the writing of detective stories. Very true to this day. In fact, most writers approach their screenplays and TV shows by working out the "Hey, what if…."

But in the article he made it sound like he was totally in control of his emotions and his art. And throughout his life, as well as his career, this was only half the truth. His passions and addictions fueled so much of his vision. And sometimes they overwhelmed him. Most of the poets who have commented on "Philosophy" agree that although they're conscious of aspects of form and structure, a passionate poem like "The Raven" could never have been written in such a meticulous and calculating manner.

But then again, Poe may just be playing us. It might be the same kind of mind game as when his most insane characters insist they're not insane. Or it may be one of the last tragic attempts of a brilliant artist to get some recognition. I wouldn't put anything past him. Remember, that's in part the way he started his career: with those Folio put-ons. Why not go out the same way?

THE BELLS

Poe's work and, sadly, his short life, come to almost a logical conclusion with "The Bells" and "Annabel Lee." They're believed to be his last two poems.

"The Bells" seems to arc over a number of phases of a person's life. But things aren't in balance. Even the length of the stanzas grow as the gloom and predicaments increase.

In Stanza I, the sweet "tinkling" and "delight," which starts the poem in such hope, is undermined with the whisper of "Runic" rhyme. Poe didn't casually choose this word. The sound of "ruin" is already present. And in II, the turtle-dove "gloats" – not a particularly positive attitude – and the sound (of the wedding bells) "dwells" on the future. But it's almost a frantic, feverish excitement. One that simply cannot last.

In Stanza III, danger and destruction are already upon us. Are the "fires" from hell or are they the burning disease that's taken from Poe every woman he's ever loved? All hope seems lost. And the bells actually sound "angry." In IV, they're more than just funeral bells. Even the dead cannot be left in peace. The "king" of demons in the tower rejoices at the pain he's caused human beings, and it's reflected in "the moaning and the groaning of the bells." Whew! Depressing.

On the upside, "The Bells" is one of the more interesting poems to read out loud. Poe was a master at matching the sounds and cadence of words with their meanings and the emotions which he wanted them to arouse.

In I, "Tinkling," "Silver," and "Icy" are all very sharp and crisp words. Things are fresh and in focus. In II, the "o" sounds predominate. "Golden," "molten," and "dove" become richer, more mellow (I chose "mellow" on purpose – pretty slick, huh?).

The "t," "k," and "ang" sounds in Stanza III have harsh and dangerous sounds to them. The "o" of "horror" and "outpour" reminds us of the way the mouth has to form a shape, just like the one in the well-known (*Home Alone*) painting "The Scream." It underscores this hell on earth.

And in IV, we're given the "om" and "o" and "um" sounds, which aren't only here in "solemn," "melancholy," "rolls," "sobbing," and "moaning," but also in the famous "Nevermore" (Pretty slick, Part II).

ANNABEL LEE (1850)

Although the general opinion was and is that "Annabel Lee" was written in memory of Poe's dead wife, Virginia, there were some women whom Poe courted after Virginia's death that believe it was written about them. Elmira Shelton, a childhood sweetheart, swore till her own death – years after Poe's – that it was about her.

Poe said he wrote it purposely in the style of an English ballad. And in fact, it's been put to music many times and recorded by dozens of singers, including Harry Belafonte.

It's believed to be his last poem, and its simple, mournful wish to be near his lost love is similar in theme to the last stanzas of "The Raven," where the grieving man asks if he can be re-united with his dead lover. The difference is that the raven's answer "Nevermore" crushes the mourning lover's spirit. It's in sharp contrast to the sweet, wish fulfilled sadness of the ending to "Annabel Lee."

Perhaps this final, nameless narrator has reached a kind of acceptance, though not totally, because he does write that the angels were jealous of their love. But there's an undeniable peacefulness and resolution to the lover's thoughts. Perhaps it was a sign that Poe wanted to believe that human beings have the ability to overcome what he felt was our inborn desire to hurt others and ourselves. We can only hope that he found some peace.
What do you think?

THE RAVEN
1845

Once upon a midnight dreary, while I pondered, weak and
    weary,
Over many a quaint and curious volume of forgotten lore —[1]
While I nodded, nearly napping, suddenly there came a
    tapping,
As of some one gently rapping, rapping at my chamber door.[2]
"'Tis some visitor," I muttered, "tapping at my chamber
    door —
        Only this and nothing more."

Ah, distinctly I remember it was in the bleak December;[3]
And each separate dying ember wrought its ghost upon the
    floor.
Eagerly I wished the morrow; — vainly I had sought to borrow
From my books surcease[4] of sorrow — sorrow for the lost
    Lenore — [5]
For the rare and radiant maiden whom the angels name
    Lenore —
        Nameless *here* for evermore.

And the silken, sad, uncertain rustling of each purple curtain
Thrilled me — filled me with fantastic terrors never felt before;[6]
So that now, to still the beating of my heart, I stood repeating
"'Tis some visiter entreating[7] entrance at my chamber door —
Some late visiter entreating entrance at my chamber door; —
        This it is and nothing more."

Presently my soul grew stronger; hesitating then no longer,
"Sir," said I, "or Madam, truly your forgiveness I implore;[8]
But the fact is I was napping, and so gently you came rapping,[9]
And so faintly you came tapping, tapping at my chamber door,
That I scarce was sure I heard you" — here I opened wide the
    door; —
        Darkness there and nothing more.[10]

1 History or ancient tales, but it also means the space between the eye and beak of a bird. Knowing Poe, he did this on purpose.

2 A chamber is, of course, a room. But there are critics who think Poe was really talking about the writer's mind, or soul.

3 Sure, December rhymes with remember, but he had a bunch of "ber" months to choose from. December is "The Holidays." If you have to feel lousy, that makes it worse, right? Note: Poe's mom died in December.

4 surcease - stopping

5 His dead wife, Virginia.

6 There again is Poe's trademark of grief and sorrow, self-torture, being perversely "thrilling."

7 entreating - begging, pleading

8 Strongly asking, begging (lots of that going on in this poem).

9 Knocking, not "hip-hopping." Although, if you think about it, this whole poem would make a totally phat rap song.

10 Poe's use of a frightening moment - straight out of the movies (which hadn't even been invented yet).

Deep into that darkness peering, long I stood there wondering, fearing,

Doubting, dreaming dreams no mortals ever dared to dream before;[1]

But the silence was unbroken, and the stillness gave no token,

And the only word there spoken was the whispered word, "Lenore?"

This I whispered, and an echo murmured back the word, "Lenore!"

Merely this and nothing more.[2]

Back into the chamber turning, all my soul within me burning,

Soon I heard a tapping somewhat louder than before.

"Surely," said I, "surely that is something at my window lattice;

Let me see, then, what thereat is, and this mystery explore —

Let my heart be still a moment and this mystery explore; —

'Tis the wind and nothing more!"[3]

Open here I flung the shutter, when, with many a flirt and flutter,

In there stepped a stately Raven of the saintly days of yore;[4]

Not the least obeisance[5] made he; not a minute stopped or stayed he;

But, with mien of lord or lady,[6] perched above my chamber door —

Perched upon a bust of Pallas[7] just above my chamber door —

Perched, and sat, and nothing more.

1 Okay, she's dead, but it seems like he's hoping here that…?

2 That'll make you have to change your shorts.

3 The second thought of every scary movie character.

4 Literary way of saying "Olden Days."

5 Showed no respect.

6 Copped an egotistical 'tude.

7 In classic mythology, Pallas was the daughter of Triton who was killed by Athena, Zeus's daughter – got that? But Poe said he just liked the way the name sounded like "pale," which contrasted with the black bird. Still, it is a name attached to a beautiful, dead woman. The guy was always thinkin'.

Then this ebony bird beguiling my sad fancy into smiling,

By the grave and stern decorum[1] of the countenance it wore,

"Though thy crest be shorn[2] and shaven, thou," I said, "art sure no craven,[3]

Ghastly grim and ancient Raven wandering from the Nightly shore —

Tell me what thy lordly name is on the Night's Plutonian[4] shore!"

      Quoth the Raven "Nevermore."

Much I marvelled this ungainly[5] fowl to hear discourse so plainly,

Though its answer little meaning — little relevancy[6] bore;

For we cannot help agreeing that no human being

Ever yet was blessed with seeing bird above his chamber door —

Bird or beast upon the sculptured bust above his chamber door,

      With such name as "Nevermore."

But the Raven, sitting lonely on the placid bust, spoke only

That one word, as if his soul in that one word he did outpour.

Nothing farther then he uttered — not a feather then he fluttered —

Till I scarcely more than muttered "Other friends have flown before —

On the morrow *he* will leave me, as my Hopes have flown before."[7]

      Then the bird said "Nevermore."

Startled at the stillness broken by reply so aptly spoken,

"Doubtless," said I, "what it utters is its only stock and store[8]

Caught from some unhappy master whom unmerciful Disaster

Followed fast and followed faster till his songs one burden bore —

Till the dirges of his Hope that melancholy burden bore

      Of 'Never — nevermore.'"[9]

1 decorum - dramatic poise and bearing

2 shorn - bald

3 No, not Wes Craven, horror flick genius. It means cowardly, but Poe would have dug Ol' Wes.

4 Pluto is God of the underworld or hell (See "The Black Cat" for the *really* bad Mickey Mouse joke).

5 ungainly - awkward

6 relevancy - relationship to anything important

7 The last two lines combine the sorrow of friends leaving – maybe dying – the sureness that the bird will leave, and a bitter comment that his hopes have also died, or left him with the death of Lenore.

8 Meaning that "Nevermore" is the bird's only "trick."

9 In the above last four lines, the narrator's trying to convince himself that the bird learned the word "nevermore" from an owner who was really beaten up by life and was without hope, as he is, also mourning a terrible loss.

But the raven still beguiling[1] all my fancy into smiling,

Straight I wheeled a cushioned seat in front of bird, and bust and door;

Then, upon the velvet sinking, I betook myself to linking

Fancy unto fancy, thinking what this ominous bird of yore —

What this grim, ungainly, ghastly, gaunt, and ominous bird of yore

   Meant in croaking "Nevermore."[2]

This I sat engaged in guessing, but no syllable expressing

To the fowl whose fiery eyes now burned into my bosom's core:

This and more I sat divining, with my head at ease reclining

On the cushion's velvet lining that the lamp-light gloated[3] o'er,

But whose velvet-violet lining with the lamp-light gloating o'er,

   She shall press, ah, nevermore![4]

Then, methought the air grew denser, perfumed from an unseen censer[5]

Swung by seraphim whose spelling foot-falls tinkled on the tufted floor.

"Wretch," I cried, "thy God hath lent thee — by these angels he[6] hath sent thee

Respite[7] — respite and nepenthe[8] from thy memories of Lenore;

Quaff, oh quaff this kind nepenthe and forget this lost Lenore!"[9]

   Quoth the Raven, "Nevermore."

"Prophet!" said I, "thing of evil! — prophet still, if bird or devil! —

Whether Tempter[10] sent, or whether tempest tossed thee here ashore,[11]

Desolate yet all undaunted,[12] on this desert land enchanted —

On this home by Horror haunted — tell me truly, I implore —

Is there — *is* there balm[13] in Gilead?[14] — tell me — tell me, I implore!"

   Quoth the Raven, "Nevermore."[15]

1 beguiling - charming

2 He's going to give himself one more chance to figure out rationally what this bird is doing there and what "Nevermore" means. Lots of luck, Sparky.

3 Here, "gloated" means it cast its light almost suffocatingly over the cushion and him.

4 He realizes that "she," the dead Lenore, will never be alive, in lamp-light again. It's here that his brain starts to circle the drain.

5 censer - A judge, but also someone who interferes with others' lives. The narrator is starting to let his fears and grief get the better of him.

6 "Thy God," and "he" kind of add up to a god with a small "h," some kind of supernatural being.

7 Respite - cut me some slack

8 nepenthe - a drug and/or painkiller

9 He's now back to feeling pain for his dead lover and wants to blot it out with drugs. Somebody also better tell him that drugs work nevermore.

10 Tempter - evil gods

11 Or if a storm or winds blew you here - it doesn't matter.

12 undaunted - fearless

13 balm - soothing comfort

14 Biblical reference to a town east of the Jordan River where a soothing ointment was made.

15 Asked if there is salvation, the Raven "tells" him…nope.

"Prophet!" said I, "thing of evil! — prophet still, if bird or
    devil!

By that Heaven that bends above us — by that God we both
    adore —

Tell this soul with sorrow laden if, within the distant Aidenn,[1]

It shall clasp a sainted maiden whom the angels name
    Lenore —

Clasp a rare and radiant maiden whom the angels name
    Lenore."[2]

        Quoth the Raven, "Nevermore."[3]

"Be that word our sign in parting, bird or fiend!" I shrieked,
    upstarting — [4]

"Get thee back into the tempest and the Night's Plutonian
    shore!

Leave no black plume as a token of that lie thy soul hath
    spoken!

Leave my loneliness unbroken! — quit the bust above my
    door!

Take thy beak from out my heart,[5] and take thy form from off
    my door!"

        Quoth the Raven "Nevermore."

And the Raven, never flitting, still is sitting, *still* is sitting

On the pallid bust of Pallas just above my chamber door;

And his eyes have all the seeming of a demon's that is
    dreaming,

And the lamp-light o'er him streaming throws his shadow on
    the floor;

And my soul from out that shadow that lies floating on the
    floor

        Shall be lifted — nevermore![6]

1 Eden – another Biblical reference.

2 He wonders if she's in Eden, or a heaven-like paradise.

3 Ouch! Cold. I don't know which one I want to smack more – the guy or the Raven.

4 That's all he wants to hear from the bird.

5 Ow!

6 So we're left with this guy feeling like his soul is trapped in permanent pain, the black shadow of the Raven evermore. Very, very grim. Well, I'm ready for a comedy flick right about now. How about you?

The Raven Notes

THE RAVEN NOTES

THE RAVEN NOTES

THE Bells
1849

I

Hear the sledges[1] with the bells —
Silver bells!
What a world of merriment their melody foretells!
How they tinkle, tinkle, tinkle,
In the icy air of night!
While the stars that oversprinkle
All the heavens, seem to twinkle
With a crystalline delight;
Keeping time, time, time,
In a sort of Runic[2] rhyme,
To the tintinnabulation[3] that so musically wells
From the bells, bells, bells, bells,
Bells, bells, bells —
From the jingling and the tinkling of the bells.

II

Hear the mellow wedding-bells —
Golden bells!
What a world of happiness their harmony foretells!
Through the balmy air of night
How they ring out their delight! —
From the molten-golden notes,
And all in tune,
What a liquid ditty floats
To the turtle-dove that listens, while she gloats
On the moon!
Oh, from out the sounding cells,
What a gush of euphony voluminously[4] wells!
How it swells!
How it dwells
On the Future! — how it tells
Of the rapture that impels[5]
To the swinging and the ringing
Of the bells, bells, bells —
Of the bells, bells, bells,bells,
Bells, bells, bells —
To the rhyming and the chiming of the bells!

1 sledges - a type of sled

2 "Runic" relates to both the ancient Scandinavian culture and the mystic rituals of the Druids.

3 tintinnabulation - chiming sounds

4 euphony voluminously - abundant harmony

5 impels - moves

III

Hear the loud alarum[1] bells —
Brazen[2] bells!
What a tale of terror, now, their turbulency[3] tells!
In the startled ear of night
How they scream out their affright!
Too much horrified to speak,
They can only shriek, shriek,
Out of tune,
In a clamorous appealing to the mercy of the fire,
In a mad expostulation[4] with the deaf and frantic fire,
Leaping higher, higher, higher,
With a desperate desire,
And a resolute endeavor,
Now — now to sit, or never,
By the side of the pale-faced moon.
Oh, the bells, bells, bells!
What a tale their terror tells
Of Despair!
How they clang, and clash, and roar!
What a horror they outpour
On the bosom of the palpitating[5]
air!
Yet the ear, it fully knows,
By the twanging,
And the clanging,
How the danger ebbs and flows;
Yet the ear distinctly tells,
In the jangling,
And the wrangling,
How the danger sinks and swells,
By the sinking or the swelling in the anger of the bells —
Of the bells —
Of the bells, bells, bells,bells,
Bells, bells, bells —
In the clamor and the clangor of the bells!

1 alarum - alarm
2 Means both brass and impudent.
3 turbulency - uproar and disruption
4 expostulation - objection
5 palpitating - breathing

IV

Hear the tolling of the bells —
Iron Bells!
What a world of solemn thought their monody[1] compels!

In the silence of the night,
How we shiver with affright
At the melancholy menace of their tone!
For every sound that floats
From the rust within their throats
Is a groan.
And the people — ah, the people —
They that dwell up in the steeple,
All alone,
And who, tolling, tolling, tolling,
In that muffled monotone,
Feel a glory in so rolling
On the human heart a stone —
They are neither man nor woman —
They are neither brute nor human —
They are Ghouls:
And their king it is who tolls: —
And he rolls, rolls, rolls,
Rolls
A paean[2] from the bells!

And his merry bosom swells
With the paean of the bells!
And he dances, and he yells;
Keeping time, time, time,
In a sort of Runic rhyme,
To the paean of the bells —
Of the bells: —
Keeping time, time, time,
In a sort of Runic rhyme,
To the throbbing of the bells —
Of the bells, bells, bells —
To the sobbing of the bells: —
Keeping time, time, time, time,
As he knells, knells, knells,
In a happy Runic rhyme,
To the rolling of the bells —

Of the bells, bells, bells: —
To the tolling of the bells —
Of the bells, bells, bells, bells,
Bells, bells, bells —
To the moaning and the groaning of the bells.[1]

1 For this poem, Poe received $15 from *Sartain's Magazine.*

THE BELLS NOTES

THE BELLS NOTES

Annabel Lee
1849

It was many and many a year ago,
    In a kingdom by the sea,
That a maiden there lived whom you may know
    By the name of Annabel Lee;—
And this maiden she lived with no other thought
    Than to love and be loved by me.

She was a child and *I* was a child,[1]
    In this kingdom by the sea,
But we loved with a love that was more than love —
    I and my Annabel Lee —
With a love that the winged seraphs[2] of Heaven
    Coveted[3] her and me.

1 Referring to his wife's age and his emotional age and innocence.

2 seraphs - angels
3 Coveted - enviously desired

And this was the reason that, long ago,
    In this kingdom by the sea,
A wind blew out of a cloud by night
    Chilling my Annabel Lee;[4]
So that her highborn kinsman came[5]
    And bore her away from me,
To shut her up in a sepulchre[6]
    In this kingdom by the sea.

4 Referring to her tuberculosis.
5 Members of their family disapproved of the marriage.
6 sepulchre - tomb

The angels, not half so happy in Heaven,
    Went envying her and me; —
Yes! that was the reason (as all men know,
    In this kingdom by the sea)
That the wind came out of a cloud, chilling
    And killing my Annabel Lee.

But our love it was stronger by far than the love
    Of those who were older than we —
Of many far wiser than we —
    And neither the angels in Heaven above
Nor the demons down under the sea,
    Can ever dissever[7] my soul from the soul
Of the beautiful Annabel Lee: —

7 dissever - dissect

For the moon never beams without bringing me dreams
    Of the beautiful Annabel Lee;
And the stars never rise but I see the bright eyes
    Of the beautiful Annabel Lee;
And so, all the night-tide, I lie down by the side
Of my darling, my darling, my life and my bride,
    In her sepulchre there by the sea —
    In her tomb by the side of the sea.

THE ANNABEL LEE NOTES

THE ANNABEL LEE NOTES